OXFORD
UNIVERSITY PRESS

ASPIRE
SUCCEED
PROGRESS

AF702560

Cambridge
Lower Secondary

Complete Mathematics 8

Sue Pemberton, Ian Bettison

Second Edition

HOMEWORK BOOK

OXFORD
UNIVERSITY PRESS

OXFORD
UNIVERSITY PRESS

Great Clarendon Street, Oxford, OX2 6DP, United Kingdom

Oxford University Press is a department of the University of Oxford.

It furthers the University's objective of excellence in research, scholarship, and education by publishing worldwide. Oxford is a registered trade mark of Oxford University Press in the UK and in certain other countries

First published in 2021

British Library Cataloguing in Publication Data
Data available

978-1-38-201886-9

10 9 8 7 6 5 4

The manufacturing process conforms to the environmental regulations of the country of origin.

Printed in the UK by Bell and Bain Ltd, Glasgow

Acknowledgements
The publisher would like to thank the following for permissions to use copyright material:

Cover: Eugene Mymrin/Getty Images

All artwork by Integra Software Services.

Every effort has been made to contact copyright holders of material reproduced in this book. Any omissions will be rectified in subsequent printings if notice is given to the publisher.

MIX
Paper | Supporting responsible forestry
FSC® C007785
FSC
www.fsc.org

Contents

1A–1C Multiplying and dividing negative integers

Example

Work out: **a** $5 \times {}^-2$ **b** ${}^-4 \times {}^-3$ **c** ${}^-4 \times 2 \times {}^-5$
d ${}^-22 \div {}^-2$ **e** ${}^-24 \div {}^-3$ **f** ${}^-40 \div 5$

---

a $5 \times {}^-2 = {}^-10$ **b** ${}^-4 \times {}^-3 = 12$ **c** ${}^-4 \times 2 \times {}^-5 = {}^-8 \times {}^-5 = 40$
d $22 \div {}^-2 = {}^-11$ **e** ${}^-24 \div {}^-3 = 8$ **f** ${}^-40 \div 5 = {}^-8$

1 Work out:

a $6 \times {}^-4$ **b** ${}^-4 \times 5$ **c** ${}^-7 \times {}^-6$ **d** $1 \times {}^-1$
e ${}^-10 \times {}^-8$ **f** ${}^-8 \times 7$ **g** ${}^-15 \times {}^-5$ **h** $22 \times {}^-8$
i ${}^-8 \times {}^-5$ **j** ${}^-6 \times {}^-11$ **k** ${}^-4 \times {}^-9$ **l** ${}^-6 \times {}^-7$
m ${}^-9 \times {}^-9$ **n** ${}^-5 \times {}^-17$ **o** ${}^-12 \times {}^-8$ **p** ${}^-15 \times {}^-14$

2 Work out:

a $16 \div {}^-4$ **b** ${}^-40 \div 5$ **c** ${}^-42 \div {}^-6$ **d** $1 \div {}^-1$
e ${}^-20 \div {}^-5$ **f** ${}^-28 \div 7$ **g** ${}^-85 \div {}^-5$ **h** $56 \div {}^-8$
i ${}^-8 \div {}^-2$ **j** ${}^-6 \div {}^-3$ **k** ${}^-24 \div {}^-6$ **l** ${}^-63 \div {}^-7$
m ${}^-45 \div {}^-3$ **n** ${}^-45 \div {}^-9$ **o** ${}^-38 \div {}^-2$ **p** ${}^-90 \div {}^-15$

3 Work out:

a ${}^-4 \times {}^-3 \times 2$ **b** ${}^-2 \times 5 \times {}^-3$ **c** $4 \times {}^-1 \times {}^-3$
d ${}^-1 \times {}^-6 \times 9$ **e** $2 \times {}^-7 \times {}^-4$ **f** ${}^-2 \times {}^-2 \times {}^-2$
g $5 \times {}^-2 \times {}^-3$ **h** ${}^-10 \times {}^-10 \times {}^-10$

4 Work out:

a $\frac{{}^-16}{4}$ **b** $\frac{{}^-24}{{}^-3}$ **c** $\frac{{}^-8}{{}^-2}$ **d** $\frac{15}{{}^-3}$
e $\frac{{}^-5}{5}$ **f** $\frac{9}{{}^-9}$ **g** $\frac{{}^-81}{3}$ **h** $\frac{{}^-75}{{}^-15}$

5 Work out: $92 \times {}^-37 \times 43 \times 0 \times {}^-17$

6 Work out: ${}^-2 \times {}^-2 \times {}^-2 \times {}^-2 \times {}^-2 \times {}^-2 \times {}^-2$

7 Work out:
a $({}^-3)^2$ **b** $({}^-7)^2$ **c** $({}^-10)^2$ **d** $({}^-21)^2$

1D Squares, cubes, roots and indices

Example

Work out:

a 8^2 **b** $(^-5)^2$ **c** $\pm\sqrt{49}$

d 5^3 **e** $(^-4)^3$ **f** $\sqrt[3]{^-8}$

---

a $8^2 = 8 \times 8 = 64$

b $(^-5)^2 = {^-5} \times {^-5} = 25$

c $\pm\sqrt{49} = 7$ or $^-7$, because $7 \times 7 = 49$ and $^-7 \times {^-7} = 49$

d $5^3 = 5 \times 5 \times 5 = 125$

e $(^-4)^3 = {^-4} \times {^-4} \times {^-4} = 16 \times {^-4} = {^-64}$

f $\sqrt[3]{^-8} = {^-2}$ because $^-2 \times {^-2} \times {^-2} = {^-8}$

1 Work out the value of:

a 2^2 **b** 3^2 **c** 7^2 **d** 15^2

e $(^-2)^2$ **f** $(^-3)^2$ **g** $(^-7)^2$ **h** $(^-15)^2$

2 Write down each of these square roots.

a $\pm\sqrt{16}$ **b** $\pm\sqrt{81}$ **c** $\pm\sqrt{9}$ **d** $\pm\sqrt{169}$

3 Use a calculator to work out the following. (Where there are two possible answers, write both.)

a 0.51^2 **b** 3.7^2 **c** $(^-5.34)^2$ **d** $(^-26.9)^2$

e $\pm\sqrt{6.76}$ **f** $\pm\sqrt{0.1156}$ **g** $\pm\sqrt{2704}$ **h** $\pm\sqrt{12.25}$

4 Use a calculator to find the value of x for each of these squares.

a

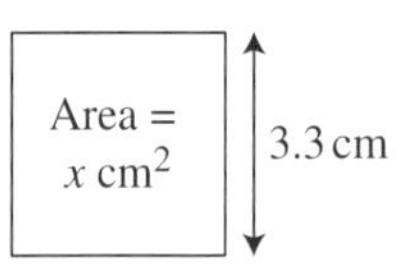

b

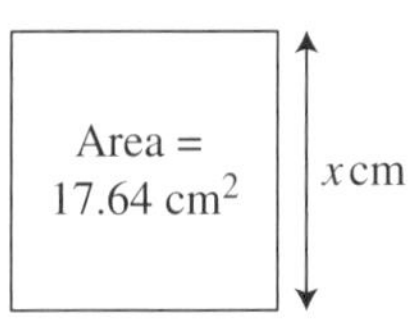

5 Work out:

a 2^2 **b** $(^-2)^2$ **c** 6^3 **d** $(^-6)^3$

e $(^-3)^3$ **f** $(^-10)^3$ **g** 0^3 **h** $(^-20)^3$

6 Write down the value of:

a $\sqrt[3]{27}$ **b** $\sqrt[3]{8}$ **c** $\sqrt[3]{^-64}$ **d** $\sqrt[3]{^-1000}$

7 Use a calculator to work out:

a 1.2^3 **b** 2.5^3 **c** $(^-6.1)^3$ **d** $(^-0.3)^3$

e $\sqrt[3]{74.088}$ **f** $\sqrt[3]{0.343}$ **g** $\sqrt[3]{4096}$ **h** $\sqrt[3]{13.824}$

8 Use a calculator to find the value of x for each of these cubes.

a

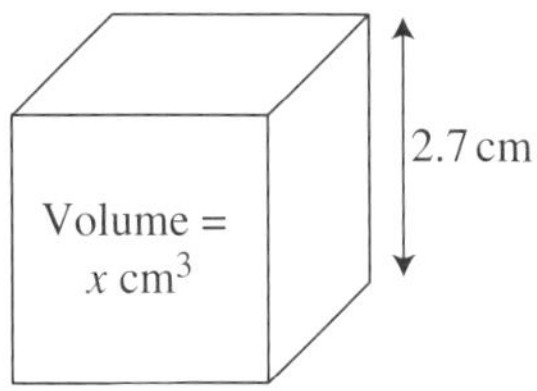

b

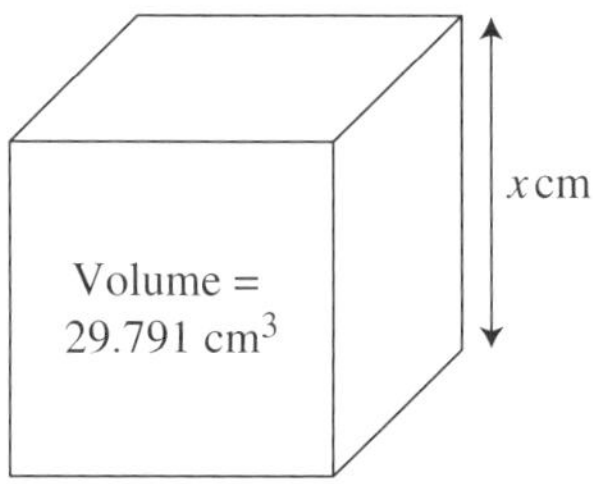

9 Work out:

a $\sqrt{\frac{9}{49}}$ **b** $\sqrt{\frac{25}{121}}$ **c** $\sqrt{\frac{64}{144}}$

d $\sqrt{0.64}$ **e** $\sqrt{1.69}$ **f** $\sqrt[3]{0.125}$

1E–1F Index notation

Example

a Write using index notation:

i $9 \times 9 \times 9 \times 9$ **ii** $2 \times 5 \times 2 \times 2 \times 2 \times 5$

b Find the value of:

i 5^4 **ii** $2^5 \times 10^4$

---

a **i** $9 \times 9 \times 9 \times 9 = 9^4$

ii $2 \times 5 \times 2 \times 2 \times 2 \times 5 = 2^4 \times 5^2$

b **i** $5^4 = 5 \times 5 \times 5 \times 5 = 625$

ii $2^5 \times 10^4 = 32 \times 10\,000 = 320\,000$

1 Write using index notation:

a $8 \times 8 \times 8 \times 8 \times 8$ **b** $4 \times 4 \times 4 \times 4 \times 4 \times 4 \times 4$

c $7 \times 7 \times 7 \times 7 \times 7 \times 7$ **d** $^{-}2 \times {}^{-}2 \times {}^{-}2 \times {}^{-}2$

e $^{-}5 \times {}^{-}5 \times {}^{-}5 \times {}^{-}5$ **f** $2 \times 2 \times 2 \times 3 \times 3$

g $2 \times 2 \times 7 \times 7 \times 7$ **h** $3 \times 5 \times 3 \times 5 \times 5 \times 5$

2 Find the value of:

a 3^4 **b** 2^4 **c** 1^8 **d** 10^4 **e** 2^5 **f** 3^5

g 4^4 **h** 2^8 **i** $(^{-}2)^5$ **j** $(^{-}3)^4$ **k** $(^{-}1)^6$ **l** $(^{-}5)^4$

3 Using the power key on your calculator, find the value of each of these. Write your answers correct to 2 decimal places.

a 1.2^4 **b** 4.7^5 **c** 2.3^6 **d** 3.1^4

e $(^{-}1.3)^4$ **f** $(^{-}6.2)^5$ **g** $(^{-}2.2)^6$ **h** $(^{-}3.1)^7$

4 Simplify these, if possible, leaving your answer in index form.

a $2^3 \times 5^3$ **b** $3^4 \times 3^7$

c $4^3 \times 5^2$ **d** $7^5 \surd 7^2$

e $18^{10} \surd 18^2$ **f** $p^8 \surd p^2$

g $3x^9 \times 2x^2$ **h** $9m^7 \surd 3m^3$

5 Write down the value of:

a 6^0 **b** $(0.8)^0$ **c** $(-4)^0$

6 Find the value of:

a $2^4 \times 5^2$ **b** $3^2 \times 2^5$ **c** $2^4 \times 10^3$ **d** $2 \times 3^2 \times 5^2$

1G–1H Prime factorisation to find HCF and LCM

Example

a Write down all the factors of 42.
b Write 84 as the product of its prime factors.

---

a Factors of 42: 1, 2, 3, 6, 7, 14, 21, 42
b

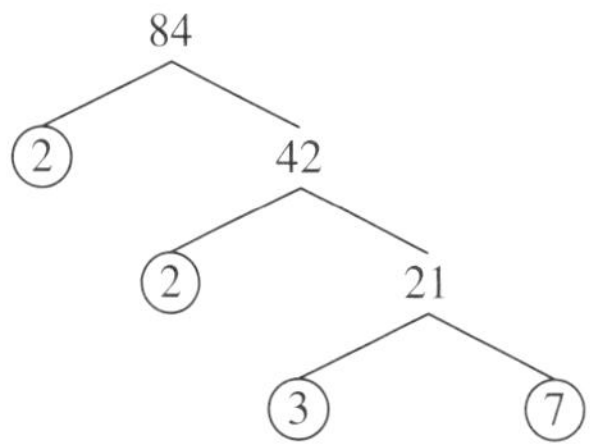

$84 = 2 \times 2 \times 3 \times 7$
$= 2^2 \times 3 \times 7$

1 Write down the first ten prime numbers.

2 Write each of these numbers as the product of their prime factors:

a 42 **b** 60 **c** 504 **d** 550

3 Find **i** the HCF **ii** the LCM of:

a 42 and 60 **b** 42 and 504 **c** 60 and 550 **d** 504 and 550

4 Find the HCF of these pairs.

a 484 and 628 **b** 735 and 960

5 Find the LCM of these pairs.

a 92 and 108 **b** 160 and 920

6 Find the HCF and LCM of:

a 12, 16 and 20 **b** 9, 15 and 24 **c** 7, 14 and 35

7 Two runners complete one lap of a track every 40 and every 50 seconds respectively. They cross the line together at 12pm. When will they next cross the line together?

8 Three pieces of wood of different lengths, 180 cm, 252 cm and 316 cm, are to be cut into equal length pieces. What is the greatest possible length of each piece?

9 A rug manufacturer has a large piece of fabric measuring 120 m by 85 m. The fabric is cut into square pieces of whole metre side length to make the minimum number of rugs. What is the side length of each rug?

10 Abi visits the supermarket every 5 days and Johan visits the same supermarket every 7 days. Abi and Johan both visit the supermarket on 1 January. Assuming their pattern stays the same, how many more times will Abi and Johan visit the supermarket on the same day in a single year?

1I Order of operations

Example

Work out: **a** $5^2 - 4 \times 3 + \sqrt{16}$ **b** $4^2 \times 10 \div (7 - 2)$

a $25 - 2 + 4 = 13 + 4 = 17$
b $16 \times 10 \div 5 = 16 \times 2 = 32$

1 Work out:

a $2 + 3 \times 8$ **b** $9 \div 3 - 8$ **c** $4^2 - 3 \times 2$ **d** $20 \div (5 - 1)$

2 Work out:

a $8^2 - 3 \times \sqrt{25}$ **b** $9 - 2.5 \times 2 + \sqrt[3]{27}$

c $2^2 \times \sqrt{16} \div (7 - 5)$ **d** $\sqrt{121} + 7 \div 2 - 9$

3 Work out:

a $(6 - 11) \times (^{-}5 + 8)$ **b** $(^{-}17 - 13) \times (^{-}19 + 25)$ **c** $8 + (^{-}9 + ^{-}3) \times 3^2$

4 Work out:

a $\sqrt{9^2 + 12^2}$ **b** $\sqrt{10^2 + 24^2}$

5 Work out:

a $\dfrac{3^2 + 8.1}{3}$ **b** $\dfrac{(8 + ^{-}4) \times 7}{14}$ **c** $\dfrac{9^2 - 3 \times 12}{6}$

6 Write brackets to make these calculations correct.

a $\sqrt{16} + 5^2 \times 10 = 290$ **b** $6 + 15 \div 3 - 7 = 0$

c $8^2 - \sqrt[3]{125} \div 10 \times 9 + 1 = 0.59$

7 Work out:

a $\dfrac{36 - (7 - 3)^2}{4 + 2 \times 3}$ **b** $\dfrac{42 + (^{-}3 - 2)^2}{6 - 5 + 2 \times 7^2}$ **c** $\dfrac{1.2 - 7 \times 0.5 + 3}{0.2 + 13 \times 0.05}$

8 In each case, use the numbers listed, plus brackets and any of the operations +, –, × and ÷ to make the target number.

a 5, 6, 7 Target: 37

b 1, 2, 3, 4 Target: 9

c 4, 5, 7, 8 Target: 79

d 3, 5, 6, 7 Target: 104

1J Natural numbers and rational numbers

Example

Here is a list of numbers.

82, ⁻4, 0.81, 16, ⁻6.8

From the list of numbers, write down all of the:

a natural numbers

b rational numbers

---

a 82, 16

b 82, ⁻4, 0.81, 16, ⁻6.8

1 Decide if each statement is true or false.

a 68 is an integer

b 68 is a natural number

c 68 is a rational number

d ⁻68 is an integer

e ⁻68 is a natural number

f ⁻68 is a rational number

g 7.2 is an integer

h 7.2 is a natural number

i 7.2 is a rational number

2 Here is a list of numbers.

91, 0.54, ⁻9, $\frac{8}{9}$, 24, ⁻2.1, 0

From this list, write down all of the:

a natural numbers

b integers

c rational numbers

d whole numbers

3 Decide if each statement is true or false.

a All integers are natural numbers.

b All whole numbers are integers.

c All rational numbers are integers.

d All natural numbers are rational numbers.

4 Jayden says that natural numbers and whole numbers are the same so there is no need to use two different names. Is Jayden correct? Explain your answer.

2A Expressions, formulae and equations

Example

A calculator costs c dollars and a cell phone costs p dollars. Write an expression for the total cost of 5 calculators and 7 cell phones.

Cost of 5 calculators $= 5 \times c = 5c$
Cost of 7 cell phones $= 7 \times p = 7p$
Total cost, in dollars, is $5c + 7p$

1 Decide if each of the following is an expression, an equation or a formula.

a $4x - 3y$ **b** $3x - 7 = 18$

c $a + 3c = F$ **d** $P - mx = g$

e $25x^2 + 3x$ **f** $4h - 9 = 2h + 2$

2 Guy is 15 years older than Colin. Colin is c years old. Write an expression for Guy's age.

3 x chocolates are shared equally between 5 people. Write an expression for the number of chocolates that each person receives.

4 Carla buys a book costing \$$b$. She pays with a \$20 note. Write an expression for the amount of change that she receives, in dollars.

5 The cost of hiring a bicycle is made up of two parts. There is a fixed charge of \$10 and a charge of \$5 for each day that the bike is hired. Write an expression for the total cost, in dollars, of hiring a bike for n days.

6 A lemon tree costs \$5 and an orange tree costs \$7. Write an expression for the total cost, in dollars, of x lemon trees and y orange trees.

7 Write an expression for the perimeter of each of these shapes.

a

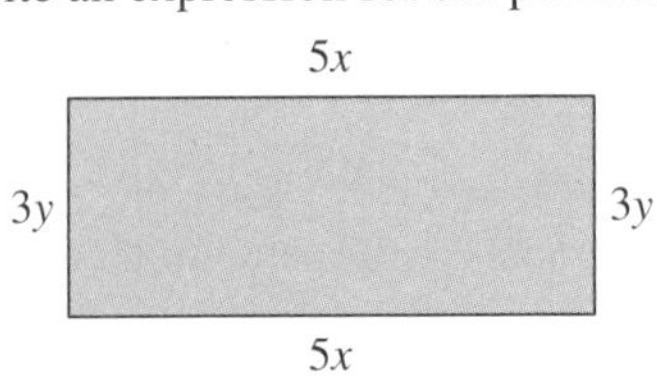

b

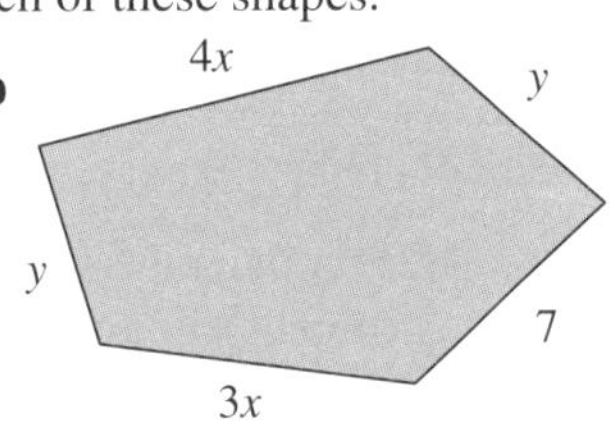

8 Martha has x apples, Nayana has 5 more apples than Martha, and Olivia has three times as many apples as Nayana.

a Find an expression for the total number of apples Martha, Nayana and Olivia have. Give your answer in its simplest form.

b **i** If Martha has 4 apples, how many apples do Martha, Nayana and Olivia have in total between them?

ii If Olivia has 75 apples, how many apples does Martha have?

9 The monthly cost of electricity is \$16, plus 7 cents for every unit used.
Write an expression for the total cost of electricity, in dollars, for a period of y months if x units are used each month.

2B Expanding brackets

Example

Expand the brackets and simplify $6(3y - 4) - 2(5y - 2)$

$$\begin{aligned} 6(3y - 4) - 2(5y - 2) &= 18y - 24 - 10y + 4 \\ &= 18y - 10y - 24 + 4 \quad \text{Collect like terms} \\ &= 8y - 20 \end{aligned}$$

1 Expand the brackets.

a $4(x + 3)$ **b** $2(3x - 4)$ **c** $3(5 - 2y)$

d $8(2y + 7)$ **e** $x(x + 2)$ **f** $y(y - 4)$

g $h(4h + 3)$ **h** $5x(7 - 3x)$ **i** $2y(3y + 5)$

2 Write down expressions for the area of each of these rectangles.

a

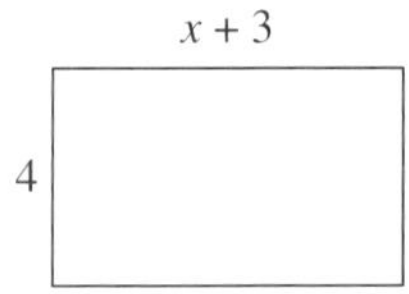

b

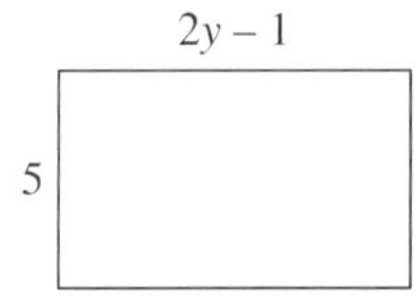

c

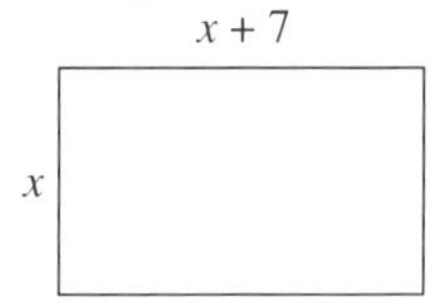

3 Expand the brackets and simplify.

a $5(x + 4) + 2(x + 3)$ **b** $3(y + 6) + 4(y - 5)$

c $2(3x - 1) + 4(2x + 3)$ **d** $6(2 - y) + 2(3 - 2y)$

e $4(2x + 3) - 3(3x + 2)$ **f** $3(x - 5) - 2(4x + 1)$

g $5(4 - 2y) - 2(6 - y)$ **h** $4(3y + 2) - 3(2y - 5)$

i $x^2(5 + 2x) + x(2 - 3x)$ **j** $2y(3 - 5y) - y(2y + 4)$

4 Work out the missing numbers.

a $3(x - \square) = 3x - 15$ **b** $\square(2x + 5) = 12x + 30$

5 Expand the brackets and simplify:

$5(x^2 - 2x) + x(2x + 7) - 4x(5 - x)$

6 Work out the area of each of the two shaded regions.

Simplify your expressions.

a

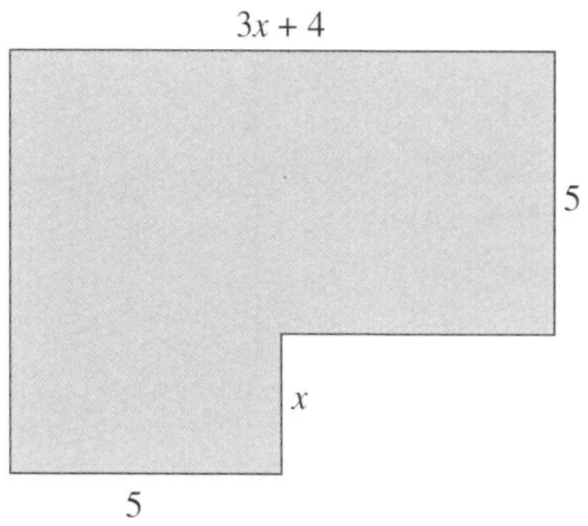

b

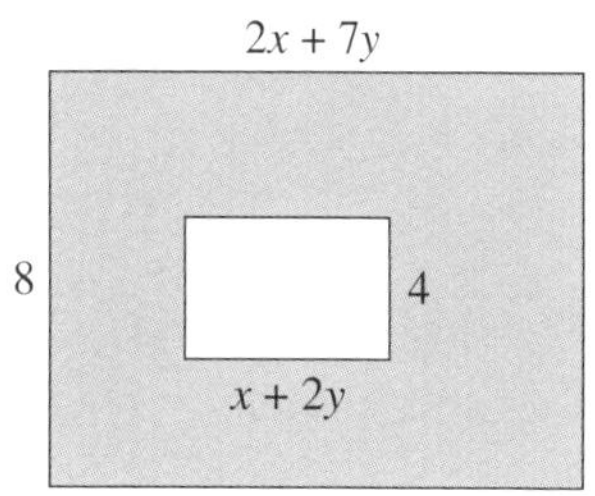

2C Factorizing expressions

Example

Factorize: **a** $6x^2 + 3x$ **b** $2ay - 3by + 3bx - 2ax$

a $3x$ is a common factor of the terms $6x^2$ and $3x$

$6x^2 + 3x = 3x(2x + 1)$

b $2ay - 3by + 3bx - 2ax = y(2a - 3b) + x(3b - 2a)$

$= y(2a - 3b) - x(2a - 3b)$

$= (y - x)(2a - 3b)$

1 Copy and complete:

a $2x - 2y = 2(\quad)$

b $10a - 15b = 5(\quad)$

c $15x - 3y + 9z = 3(\quad)$

d $px + py - pz = p(\quad)$

e $2xa - xb = x(\quad)$

f $3lx - 6ly = 3l(\quad)$

2 Copy and complete:

a $cy - dy = (\quad)y$

b $3mz - lnz + 2pz = (\quad)z$

c $2x + 4xy + 6x^2 = 2x(\quad)$

3 Factorize:

a $2x - 2y$

b $5x - 20y$

c $ax - ay$

d $px - 2py + 7pz$

e $3ax - 4bx + 2cx$

f $6ax + 4bx + 2cx$

g $6x^2 + 3x + 9xy$

h $5x^2 + 10x^2y - 15xy^2$

i $x^2 - 5x$

4 Factorize:

a $x^3 - 6xy$

b $a^2b^3c - ab^2c$

c $27y - 9y^3 + 3y^4$

d $x^3yz + x^2yz^2 - xy^2z^3$

e $7abcd - 21bcde + 14cdef$

f $-8x^3y^4z^2 - 16x^2y^3z^4 + 4x^4y^2z^3$

5 Expand the brackets, simplify, and factorize:

a $x(y - 2) + 3x(6 - y) - 7xy$

b $ab(6a + b) - 3a^2(b - 2) + 2b(a^2 + 1)$

6 The area of this rectangle is $15x^2 + 35x$.

$3x + 7$

Find an expression for the perimeter of the rectangle in its simplest form.

7 The area of a rectangle is $12x^2 + 42x$.

The perimeter of the same rectangle is $16x + 14$.

Find an expression for the two side lengths of the rectangle.

2D Substitution into expressions

Example

If $a = 4$ and $b = {}^-6$, find the value of $2b^2 - 3ab$.

$$\begin{aligned} 2b^2 - 3ab &= 2 \times ({}^-6)^2 - (3 \times 4 \times {}^-6) \\ &= 2 \times 36 - ({}^-72) \\ &= 72 + 72 \\ &= 144 \end{aligned}$$

1 If $x = 3$ and $y = 5$, find the value of:

a $2x + 3y$ **b** $xy + 6$ **c** $50 - 2xy$

d $2x(y - 2)$ **e** $3(x - y + 7)$ **f** $4xy - 2x$

g $\frac{2xy}{6}$ **h** $\frac{4y - 2x}{7}$ **i** $\frac{x + y}{x - y}$

j $2x^2 + 5$ **k** $4y^2 - 3$ **l** $y^3 + 2x$

m $3(x^2 + 8)$ **n** $x^3 - y^2$ **o** $2y^2 - x^3$

p $20y - 2x^3$ **q** $38 + 3y^3$ **r** $8y^2 - 5x^2 - 7$

2 If $x = {}^-2$, $y = {}^-3$ and $z = {}^-4$, find the value of:

a $5x + 4y + 3z$ **b** $2xyz$ **c** $x^2 + y^2 + z^2$

d $2xy + 3yz$ **e** $4(2x - 3y + z)$ **f** $3x^2 + 5$

g $\frac{8xy}{z}$ **h** $\frac{x + y}{x - y}$ **i** $\frac{8 - 2y + 3x}{z}$

j $x^2 + 2x - 8$ **k** $3y^2 - 3y + 2$ **l** $2z^2 + 5z - 1$

m $x^3 - 9$ **n** $2x^3 - 3x$ **o** $3z^3 + 2z^2$

p $200 - 4y^3$ **q** $7xy - z^3$ **r** $3x^4 - 7x^2$

3 Write down the value of:

a $({}^-1)^{16}$ **b** $({}^-1)^{25}$ **c** $({}^-1)^{31}$

d $({}^-1)^{40}$ **e** $({}^-1)^{64}$ **f** $({}^-1)^{201}$

4 Find the odd one out when $x = {}^-4$ and $y = 3$.

$3x^2 + y$	$(xy - x)^3$	$3(x^2 + y - 2)$

5 Which of these expressions have the same value when $x = 4$ and $y = {}^-5$?

$3x + y^2$ ${}^-5xy$ $x^2 - y$ $3y^2 - 5y$

6 **a** Work out the mean of these four expressions.

$3x + 7$ $\quad$ $2x - 3$ $\quad$ $x + 5$ $\quad$ $2x - 5$

b Choose a value for x and substitute it into each expression and then find the mean. Now substitute your value for x into the expression you worked out for part **a**. Check your two answers are the same.

c Does it matter what value of x you choose for part **b**?

3A Quadrilaterals

Example

Write down the number of equal sides and the number of equal angles in:

a a rectangle **b** a rhombus

a A rectangle has two pairs of equal sides and four equal angles.

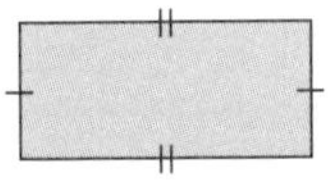

b A rhombus has two pairs of equal angles and all four sides are the same length.

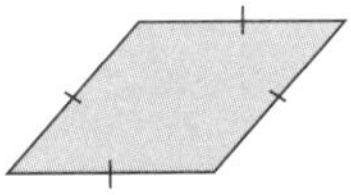

1 Write down the name of each quadrilateral from the description.

a All four sides are equal in length and the diagonals are equal in length.

b Adjacent sides are equal in length and the diagonals bisect each other.

c Opposite sides are equal in length and the diagonals are equal in length.

d There is one pair of parallel sides.

2 Write down the names of the quadrilaterals whose sides are of equal length.

3 Write down the names of the quadrilaterals whose diagonals bisect their angles.

4 Write down the names of the quadrilaterals whose diagonals are **not** equal in length.

5 Are these statements true or false?

a All squares are rectangles.

b All parallelograms are rhombuses.

c All rhombuses are squares.

d All kites are trapeziums.

6 AC and BD are diagonals of a quadrilateral intersecting at O.
Write down the names of the possible quadrilaterals if:

a OA = OC, OB = OD and angle AOB = 90°

b OA = OC, OB = OD and angle AOB ≠ 90°

c AC = BD

3B–3C 3D shapes

Example

Draw the plan, front elevation and side elevation of this object:

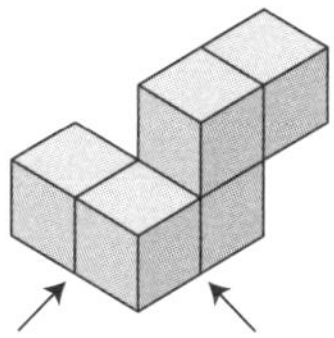

Front Side

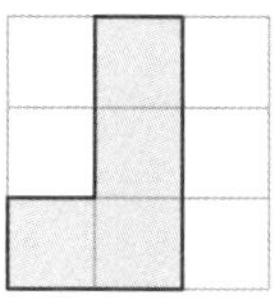

Plan

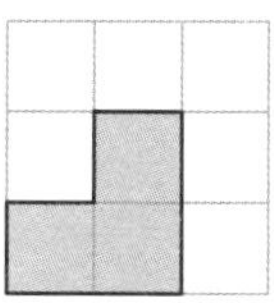

Front

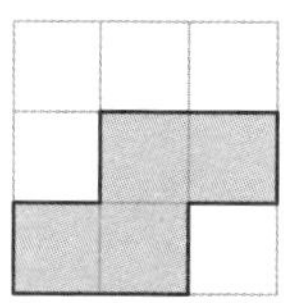

Side

1 A polyhedron has 12 vertices and 8 faces.
How many edges does it have?

2 Use isometric paper to draw the 3D shape represented by this plan and elevations.

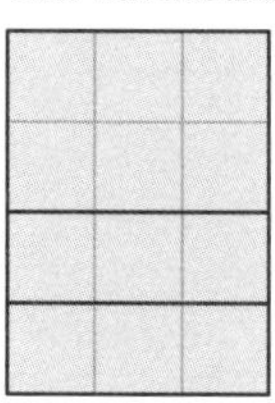

Plan

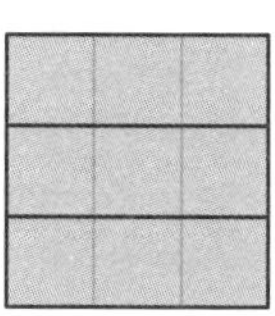

Front

Side

For questions **3** and **4**, draw the plan, the front and the side elevations.

3

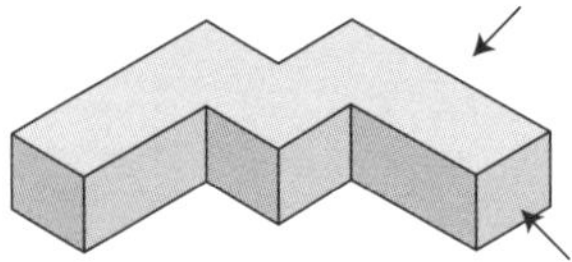

4

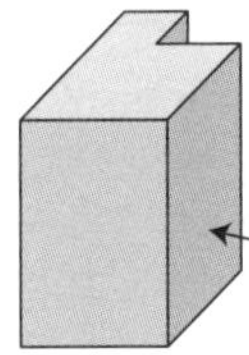

5 The distance between four European cities is as follows.

Budapest			
183 km	**Bratislava**		
229 km	55 km	**Vienna**	
476 km	296 km	263 km	**Prague**

What is the distance on a map with a scale of 1 : 500 000:

a from Budapest to Bratislava

b from Vienna to Prague

c from Vienna to Budapest?

6 A more detailed map has a scale of 1 : 100 000. Find the actual distance between two places if the distance on the map is:

a 1 cm **b** 10 cm **c** 0.5 cm

Find the map distance if the actual distance is:

d 15 km **e** 8 km **f** 25 km

7 Axel drew a plan of his classroom using a scale of 5 cm to represent 1 m.

a Write the scale Axel used in the form $1 : n$.

b On the plan, the length of the classroom is 27 cm. What is the actual length of the classroom?

c The actual width of the classroom is 5.1 m. What is the width of the classroom on the plan?

8 A plan of a field is to be drawn using a scale of 1 : 5000. Two trees in the field are 420 metres apart. How far apart will they be on the plan?

3D Bearings

Example

An aircraft travels from Melbourne, Australia, on a bearing of 060°, for a distance of 200 km. Show this in a diagram using 1 cm to represent 50 km.

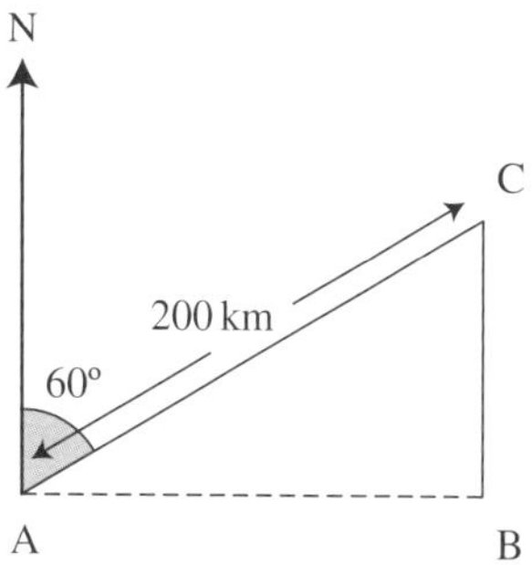

1 Draw a diagram for each of these bearings.

a 165° **b** 020° **c** 230°
d 315° **e** 172° **f** 270°

2 Write down the bearing of:

a East **b** South West
c North West **d** North

3 A ship travels from port A to port B along a bearing of 320°. Find the bearing that the ship would need to sail on to return directly from port B to port A.

4 A yacht sails on a bearing of 040° for 4000 m and then a further 3000 m on a bearing of 110°. Make a scale drawing and then find:

a the distance of the yacht from its starting position

b the bearing on which it must sail to return directly to its starting position.

3E–3G Constructions

Example

Construct accurately triangle ABC, where AB = 5 cm, BC = 4 cm and AC = 3 cm.

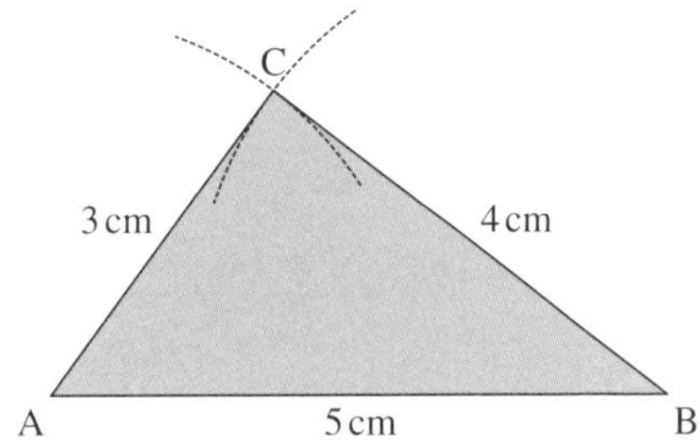

1 Construct these triangles accurately.
Find the lengths of the sides marked x.

a

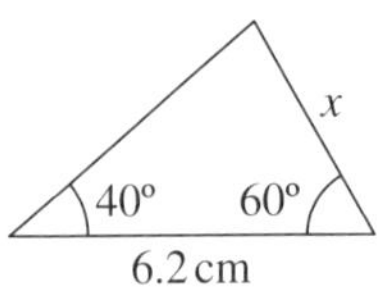

b

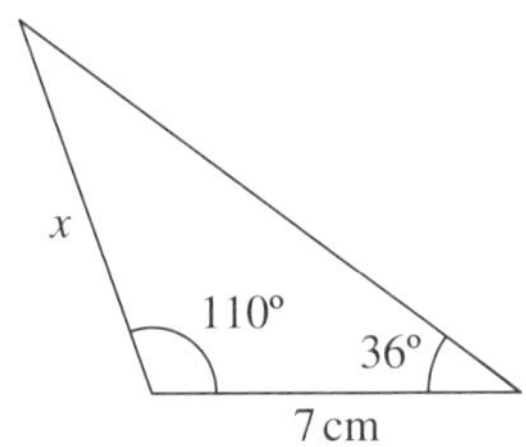

2 Construct these triangles accurately.
Find the size of the angles marked x.

a

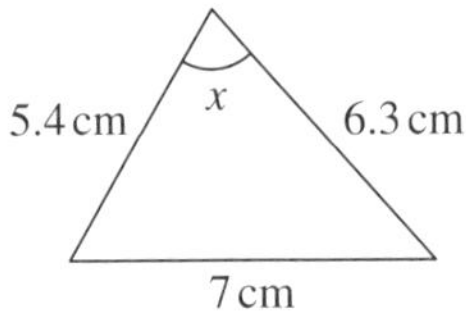

b

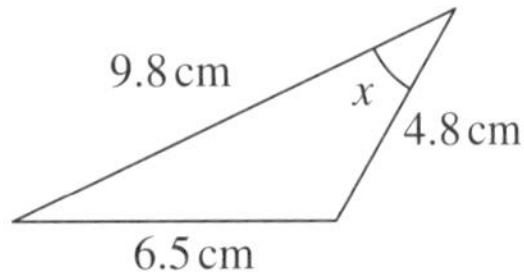

3 Construct these right-angled triangles.

a ABC where AB = 5 cm and the hypotenuse BC = 6 cm

b PQR where PQ = 8 cm and the hypotenuse QR = 12 cm

c JKL where JK = 6.5 cm and the hypotenuse KL = 9.4 cm

4 Construct these shapes.
Find x for each shape.

a

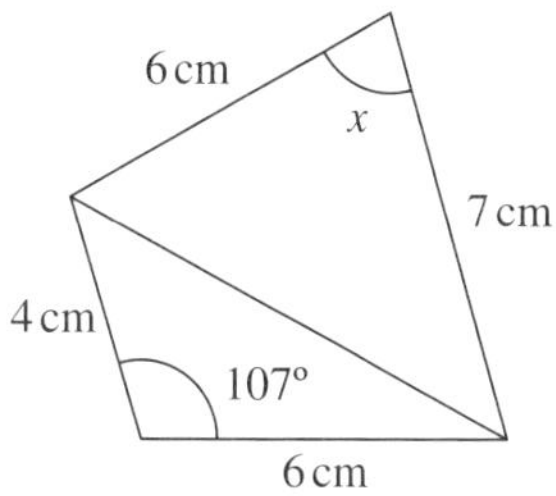

b

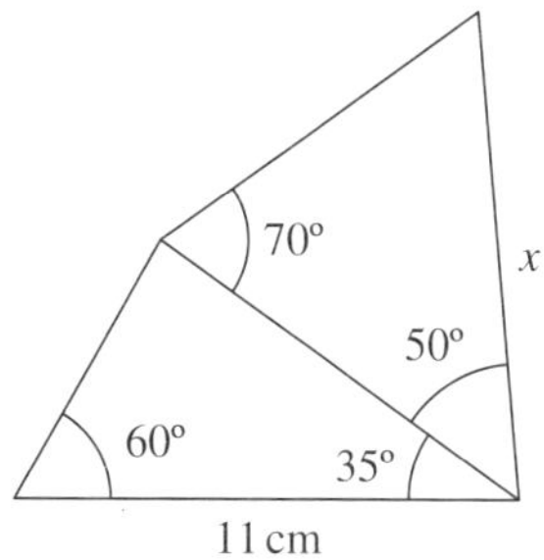

5 Explain why it is not possible to construct a triangle with sides 11 cm, 6 cm and 4 cm.

3H–3I Bisecting angles and lines

Example

Construct the perpendicular bisector of the line AB.

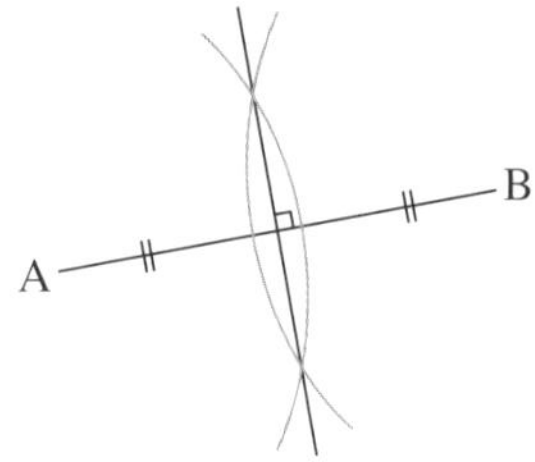

1 Draw an approximate copy of each angle.
Use compasses and a straight edge to bisect it.

a

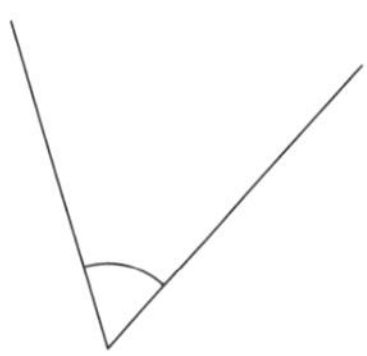

b

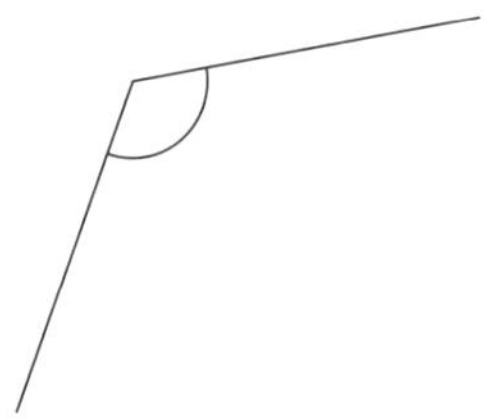

2 Copy these lines. (When you copy the lines keep them at approximately the angles shown.)
Use compasses and a straight edge to draw the perpendicular bisector of each line.

a

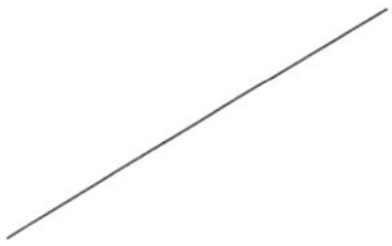

b

3 **a** Draw this triangle accurately.

b Use compasses and a straight edge to draw the perpendicular bisector of each side. All your lines should meet at the same point.

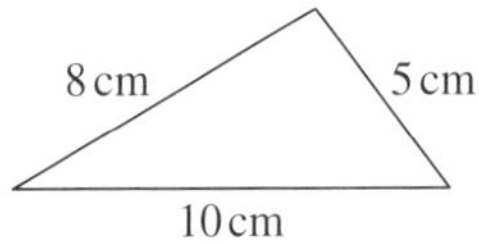

c Use the point where your three perpendicular bisectors intersect to draw a circle that goes through every vertex of the triangle.

4 **a** Draw this triangle accurately.

b Use compasses and a straight edge to draw the angle bisector of each angle. All your lines should meet at the same point.

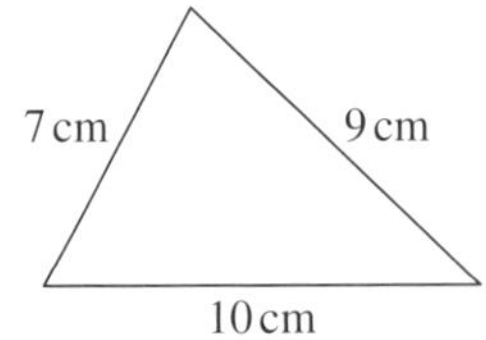

c Use the point where your three angle bisectors intersect to draw a circle that just touches the sides of the triangle.

4A Methods of data collection

Example

Write down five different ways of collecting data.

There are many different ways of collecting data and they include:

- questionnaires
- data collection sheets
- observation
- interviews
- opinion polls
- focus groups.

1 Copy the table and write three advantages or disadvantages in each section.

Method of collecting data	Advantages	Disadvantages
Questionnaire/data collection sheet	1 2 3	1 2 3
Interview	1 2 3	1 2 3

2 Mr Barnes is the owner of a large chain of gyms.

He wants to find out which gyms are bringing in the most customers and the most income. He decides to look at the membership records for each gym.

Give one advantage and one disadvantage of using secondary sources, such as the membership records, as a method of data collection.

3 Giovanna thinks that the most popular type of food in Italy is grilled fish.

a Explain why carrying out interviews would not be an appropriate method of data collection.

b What method of data collection do you think Giovanna should use?

4B Sampling methods

Example

Describe two ways in which Faria could take a random sample of five students from her class.

Method 1:
She could get a numbered list of students and then use a random number generator to select the students for the sample.

Method 2:
She could put all of the names in a 'hat' and draw out five names.

1 Alicia wants to find out what the students in her school think of the lunches.

She is considering the sampling methods in **a** to **d**. Name these methods and give an advantage and a disadvantage of each.

a Ask the first 20 students she sees one morning.

b Get an ordered list of students, and choose 20 students by generating random numbers.

c Choose four students, at random, from each of the five year groups.

d Choose one form at random and ask every student in that form.

2 Malik wants to find out about people's attitude to a proposed new airport near his town. He has two possible methods for sampling.

Method 1: Ask the first 25 men and the first 25 women he sees in the street one Monday morning.

Method 2: Get an ordered list of residents in the town and choose 50 people by generating random numbers.

a What is the name of sampling method 1?

b What is the name of sampling method 2?

c Give one advantage of each of these sampling methods.

d Give one disadvantage of each of these sampling methods.

3 Arturo is the manager of a sports club.

The sports club has 85 members who are female and 65 members who are male.

He wants to find out the opinion of club members about the changing facilities.

a Explain why a stratified sample is better than a simple random sample in this case.

b Explain how Arturo can take a stratified sample of size 30.

5A Circumference of a circle

Example

Find the circumference of a circle with diameter 11 cm.
Use $\pi = 3.14$

$$\begin{aligned}\text{Circumference} &= \pi \times \text{diameter}\\ &= 3.14 \times 11 \text{ cm}\\ &= 34.54 \text{ cm}\end{aligned}$$

Use $\pi = 3.14$ in these questions.

1 Calculate the circumference of a circle with a diameter of:

a 3 cm **b** 7 cm **c** 15 cm **d** 28 cm

2 Calculate the circumference of a circle with a radius of:

a 6 cm **b** 9 cm **c** 14 cm **d** 31 cm

3 Find the perimeter of each shape.

a

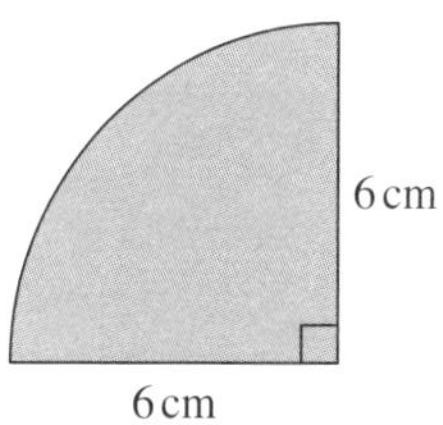

b

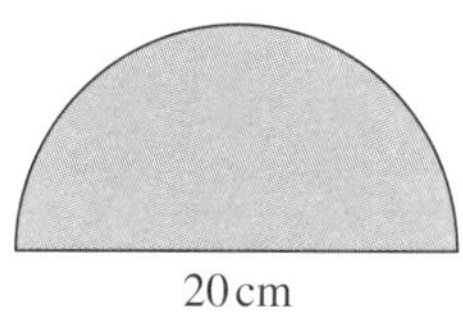

c

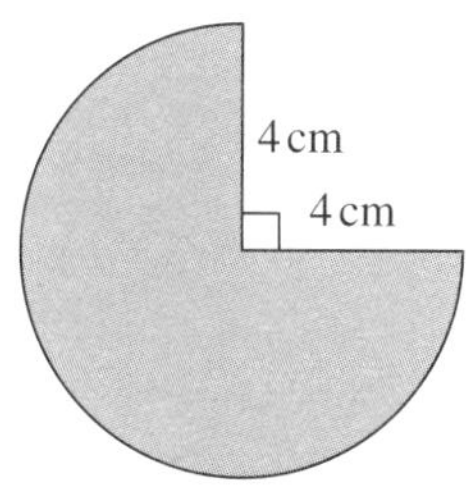

d

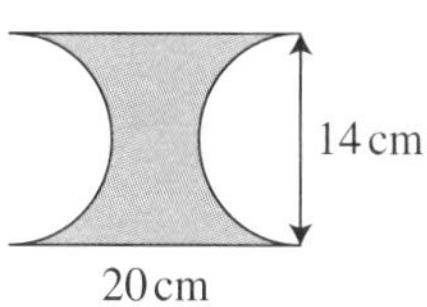

e

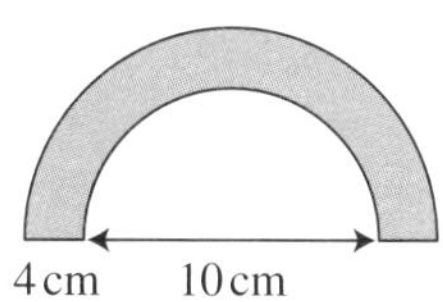

f

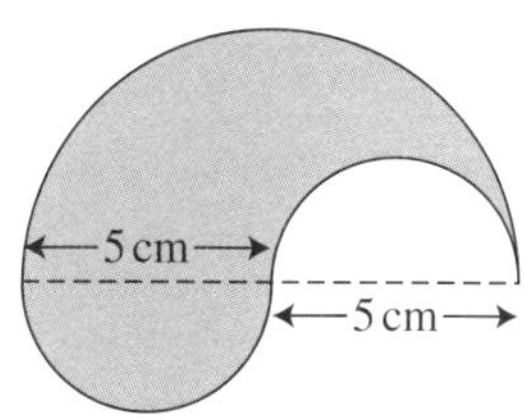

4 The circumference of a circle is 80 cm.
Calculate the diameter of the circle.

5 The circumference of a circle is 120 cm.
Calculate the radius of the circle.

5B–5D Areas of parallelograms and trapeziums

Example

Find the area of the shape.

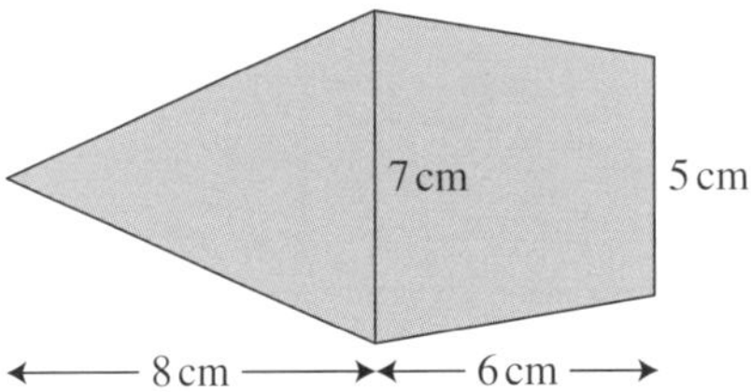

Area of triangle $= \frac{1}{2} \times 7 \times 8 = 28\,\text{cm}^2$

Area of trapezium $= \frac{1}{2} \times (7 + 5) \times 6 = 36\,\text{cm}^2$

Total area $= 28 + 36 = 64\,\text{cm}^2$

1 Find the area of each parallelogram.

a

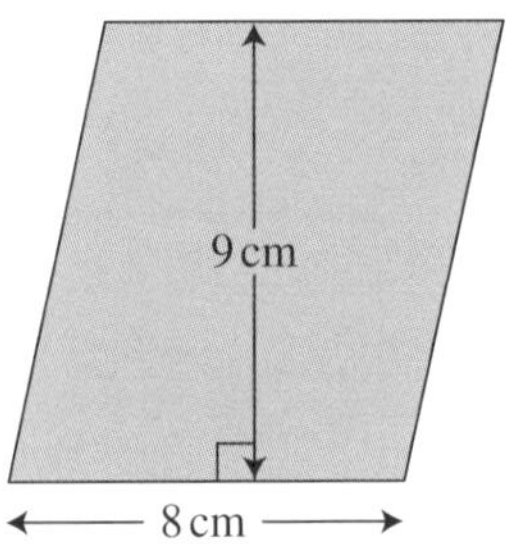

b

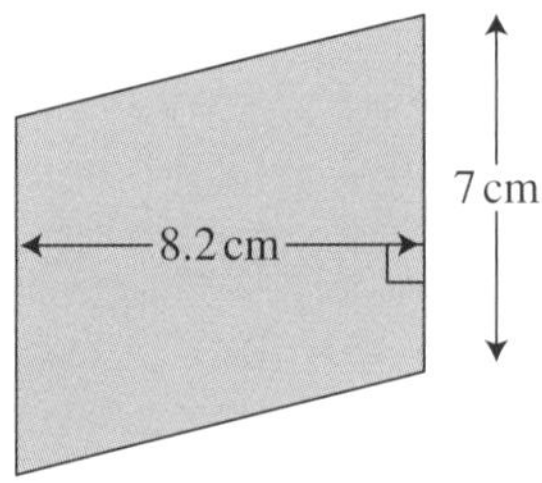

2 Find the area of each trapezium.

a

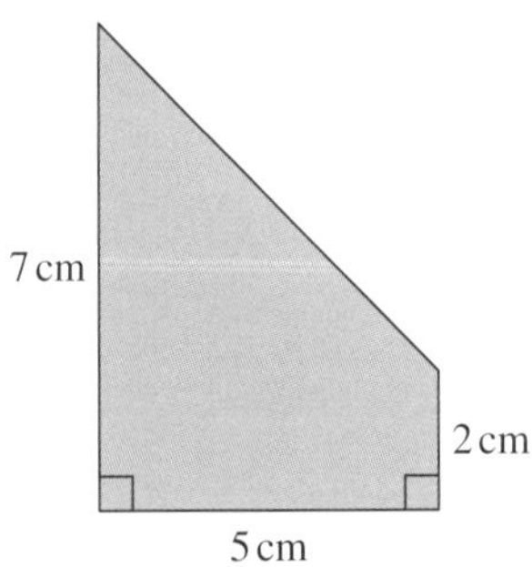

b

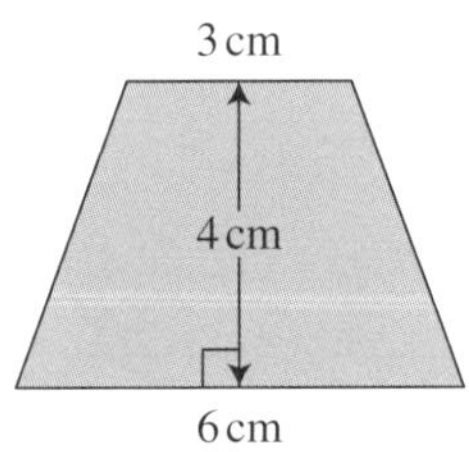

3 A trapezium has parallel sides that measure 15 cm and 22 cm.
The perpendicular distance between the two parallel sides is 9 cm.
Find the area of the trapezium.

4 The area of a trapezium is $72\,\text{cm}^2$.
The two parallel sides measure 6 cm and 12 cm.
Find the perpendicular distance between the two parallel sides.

5 Find the area of each shape.

a

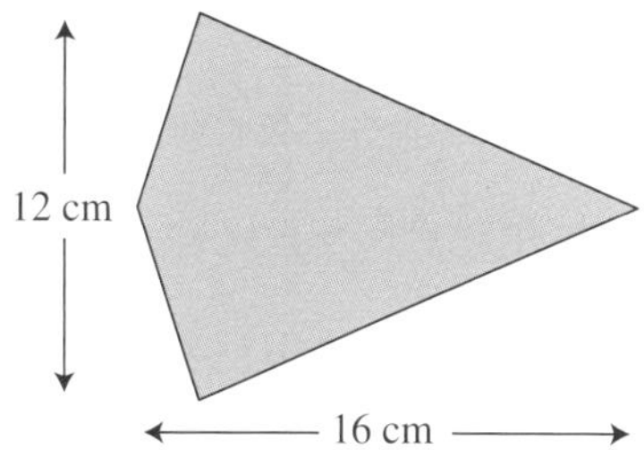

b

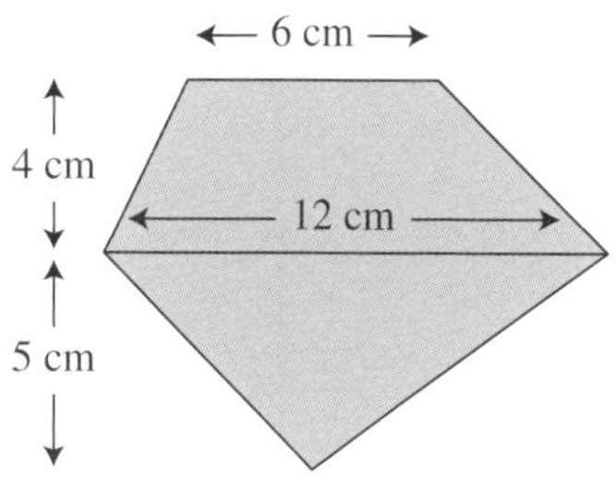

5E Volume of a triangular prism

Example

Find the volume of this prism.

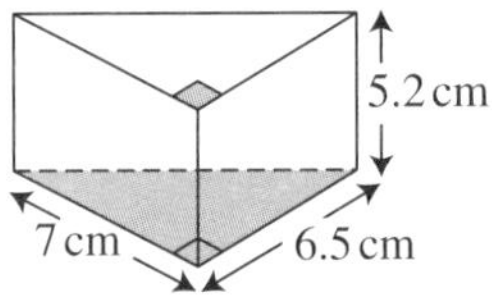

The base is a triangle.

Area of base triangle, $A = \frac{1}{2} b \times h$

$= \frac{1}{2} \times 6.5\,\text{cm} \times 7\,\text{cm}$

$= 22.75\,\text{cm}^2$

Volume of prism $= A \times h$

$= 22.75\,\text{cm}^2 \times 5.2\,\text{cm}$

$= 118.3\,\text{cm}^3$

1 Find the volume of these triangular prisms.

a

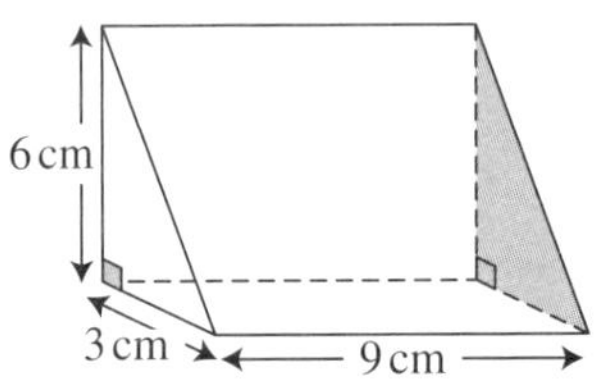

b

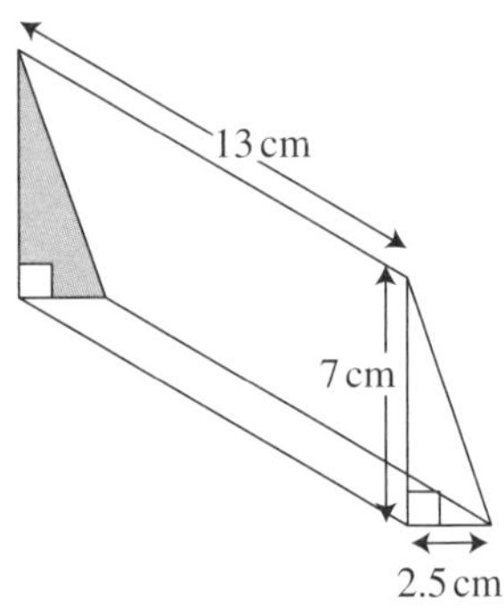

2 Find the volume of a triangular prism with cross-sectional area $8\,\text{cm}^2$ and length 24 cm.

3 A triangular prism has volume $820\,\text{cm}^3$. The length of the prism is 20 cm.

Find the area of the triangular cross-section.

4 Calculate the missing side length for this triangular prism with volume $276\,\text{cm}^3$.

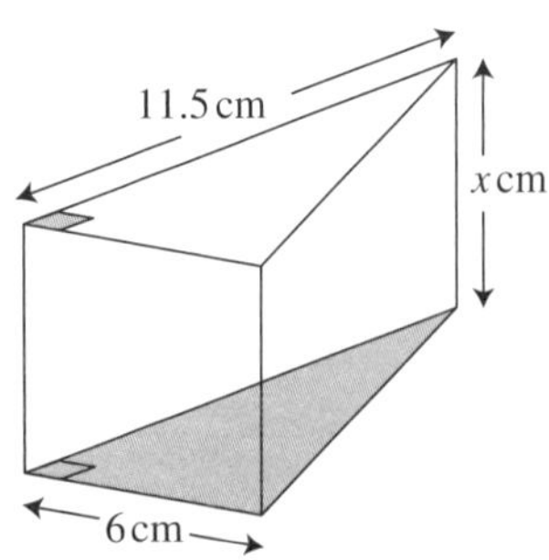

5E Surface area of prisms and pyramids

Example

Find the surface area of this cuboid.

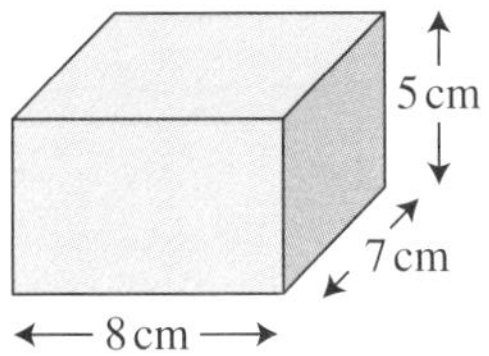

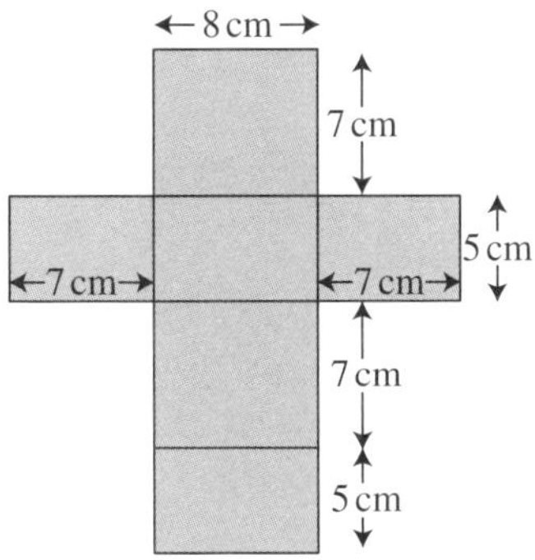

Surface area = $(7 \times 8) + (5 \times 8) + (7 \times 8) + (5 \times 8)$
$+ (5 \times 7) + (5 \times 7)$
$= 56 + 40 + 56 + 40 + 35 + 35 = 262\ \text{cm}^2$

1 Draw the nets of these cuboids and work out their surface areas.

a

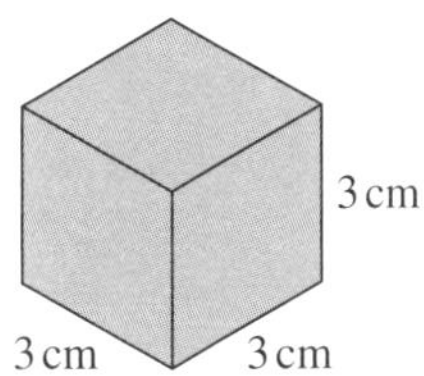

b

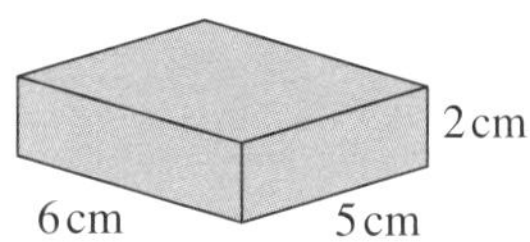

c

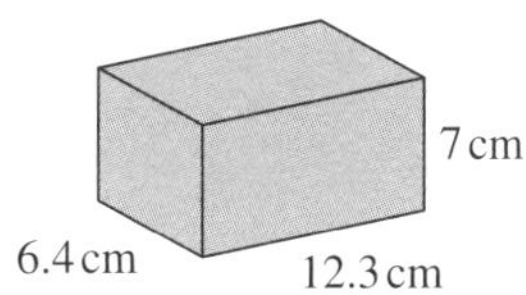

2 The diagrams show a square-based pyramid and its net.

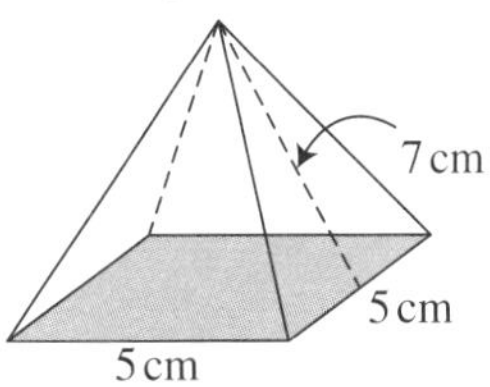

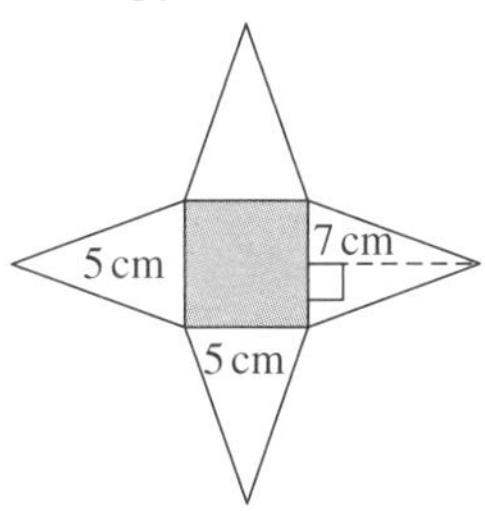

Use the net to work out the surface area of the pyramid.

3 The diagram shows a triangular prism and its net.

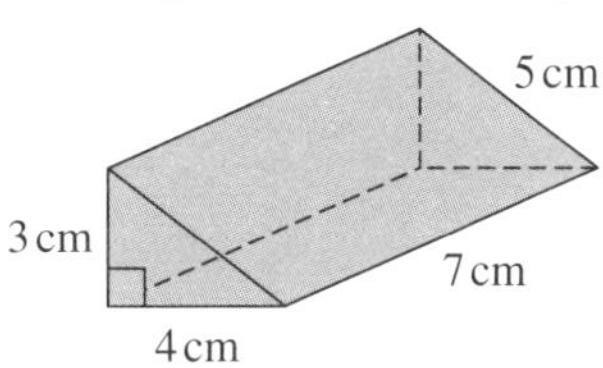

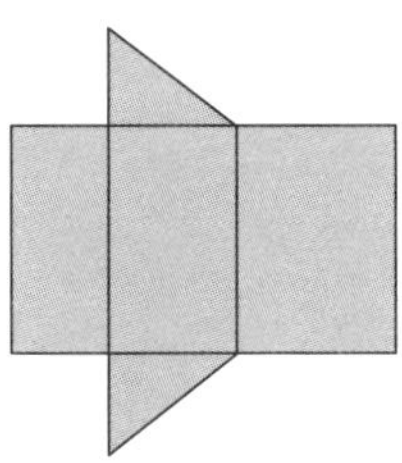

Use the net to work out the surface area.

4 Find the surface area of this T-shaped prism.

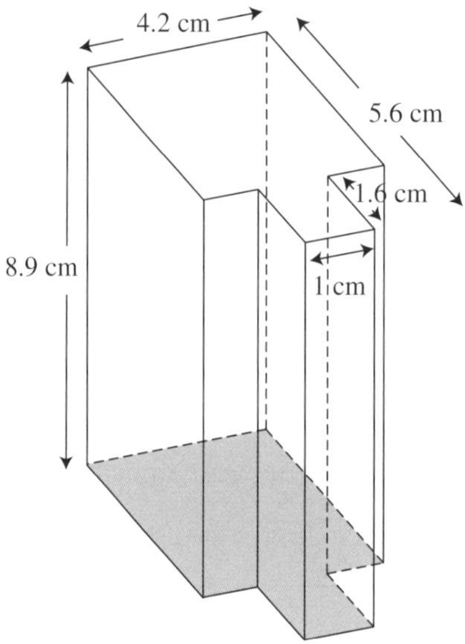

5G Imperial units

Example

Change 120 miles to kilometres.

Remember:
1 km $\approx \frac{5}{8}$ mile

---

1 mile $\oplus \frac{8}{5}$ km

120 miles $\approx 120 \times \frac{8}{5}$ km $= (120 \div 5) \times 8$ km

$= 24 \times 8$ km

$= 192$ km

1 Copy and complete:

a 1 km ≈ □ miles **b** 8 km ≈ □ miles

2 Copy and complete:

a 10 miles ≈ □ km **b** 20 miles ≈ □ km

c 25 miles ≈ □ km **d** 15 miles ≈ □ km

e 60 miles ≈ □ km **f** 45 miles ≈ □ km

g 150 miles ≈ □ km **h** 315 miles ≈ □ km

3 Copy and complete:

a 24 km ≈ □ miles **b** 48 km ≈ □ miles

c 56 km ≈ □ miles **d** 80 km ≈ □ miles

e 64 km ≈ □ miles **f** 112 km ≈ □ miles

g 400 km ≈ □ miles **h** 172 km ≈ □ miles

4 The distance between Bangalore and Mumbai is 838 km.
Approximately how many miles is this?

5 A car is travelling at 63 miles per hour.
Approximately how many kilometres per hour is this?

6A–6C Multiplying and dividing decimals

Example

Work out: **a** 35×0.1 **b** 5.6×0.01 **c** $23 \div 0.1$ **d** $7.26 \div 0.01$

a $35 \times 0.1 = 35 \div 10 = 3.5$ **b** $5.6 \times 0.01 = 5.6 \div 100 = 0.056$

c $23 \div 0.1 = 23 \times 10 = 230$ **d** $7.26 \div 0.01 = 7.26 \times 100 = 726$

1 Work out:

a 5.3×100 **b** 5.6×10 **c** 0.6×1000 **d** 2.5×100

e 0.07×10 **f** 0.005×100 **g** 0.22×1000 **h** 4.4×1000

i 5.4×1000 **j** 0.09×100 **k** 3.03×100 **l** 5.9×100

2 Work out:

a $6.4 \div 100$ **b** $8 \div 10$ **c** $5.8 \div 1000$ **d** $0.4 \div 100$

e $0.24 \div 10$ **f** $0.087 \div 100$ **g** $0.72 \div 1000$ **h** $0.003 \div 1000$

i $0.8 \div 1000$ **j** $0.27 \div 100$ **k** $0.05 \div 10$ **l** $1.04 \div 100$

3 Write the answers to these calculations as decimals:

a $5 \times \frac{1}{10}$ **b** $6 \times \frac{1}{100}$ **c** $52 \times \frac{1}{1000}$ **d** $345 \times \frac{1}{100}$

4 Work out:

a 54×0.1 **b** 5.62×0.1 **c** 6×0.1 **d** 45×0.1

e 8×0.1 **f** 0.1×5.2 **g** 0.01×5 **h** 0.01×0.3

i 15×0.01 **j** 456×0.01 **k** 0.2×0.01 **l** 76×0.01

5 Work out:

a 7×0.2 **b** 4×0.3 **c** 8×0.7 **d** 7×0.5

e 3×0.6 **f** 11×0.8 **g** 7×0.04 **h** 6×0.06

i 5×0.04 **j** 0.09×8 **k** 0.03×9 **l** 0.02×14

6 Work out:

a $62 \div 0.1$ **b** $8 \div 0.1$ **c** $6.3 \div 0.1$ **d** $15 \div 0.1$

e $0.24 \div 0.1$ **f** $0.03 \div 0.1$ **g** $8 \div 0.01$ **h** $7 \div 0.01$

i $12 \div 0.01$ **j** $0.6 \div 0.01$ **k** $3.5 \div 0.01$ **l** $22 \div 0.01$

6D–6E Significant figures

Example

Write 75 682 to:

a 2 s.f. **b** 3 s.f.

The column heads are:

TTh	Th	H	T	U
7	5	6	8	2

a The second digit head is thousands so round to the nearest thousand: 75 682 = 76 000 (2 s.f.)

b The third digit head is hundreds so round to the nearest hundred: 75 682 = 75 700 (3 s.f.)

1 Write correct to 1 significant figure:

a 58 **b** 267 **c** 5.32 **d** 13 629 **e** 0.00021 **f** 70.999

2 Write correct to 2 significant figures:

a 976 **b** 599 **c** 5381 **d** 36.94 **e** 0.00195 **f** 6.039

3 Copy and complete:

Number	457 213	5.8612	0.004851
3 s.f.			
2 s.f.			
1 s.f.			

4 Round 7 243 589 to:

a 4 s.f. **b** 3 s.f. **c** 2 s.f. **d** 1 s.f.

5 A number rounded to 1 s.f. is 10 000. What is the

a largest number it could have been

b smallest number it could have been?

6 Change these fractions to decimals.

a $\frac{2}{11}$ **b** $\frac{4}{7}$ **c** $\frac{5}{9}$

In Question **7** decide whether or not to round your answer.

Explain your choice. You may use a calculator.

7 What is the volume of a cuboid with length 11.15 cm, width 21.76 cm and height 9.5 cm?

6F–6H Recurring decimals

Example

Change $\frac{4}{15}$ to a decimal.

$\frac{4}{15} = 4 \div 15$

$= 0.2666...$

$= 0.2\dot{6}$

$$\begin{array}{r} 0.\ 2\ 6\ 6\ 6... \\ 15\overline{)4.{}^{4}0^{10}0^{10}0^{10}0...} \end{array}$$

1 Convert these fractions to decimals.

a $\frac{1}{2}$ **b** $\frac{3}{8}$ **c** $\frac{5}{16}$ **d** $\frac{9}{20}$ **e** $\frac{14}{25}$

2 Write these numbers using recurring decimal notation and convert them to fractions. Cancel them to their simplest form if necessary.

a 0.888 … **b** 0.222 …

c 0.252525 … **d** 0.414141 …

e 0.265265265 … **f** 0.030303 …

3 Convert these fractions to decimals.

a $\frac{2}{3}$ **b** $\frac{5}{6}$ **c** $\frac{2}{9}$ **d** $\frac{7}{9}$ **e** $\frac{3}{11}$

f $\frac{7}{11}$ **g** $\frac{5}{7}$ **h** $\frac{3}{14}$ **i** $\frac{7}{12}$ **j** $\frac{4}{13}$

4 **a** $2\frac{1}{3}$ **b** $5\frac{1}{6}$ **c** $10\frac{5}{9}$ **d** $8\frac{2}{11}$ **e** $3\frac{6}{7}$

5 By converting to fractions with a common denominator, find which fraction is larger in each pair.

a $\frac{3}{8}$ or $\frac{1}{3}$ **b** $\frac{4}{9}$ or $\frac{2}{5}$ **c** $\frac{4}{5}$ or $\frac{5}{6}$ **d** $\frac{4}{7}$ or $\frac{2}{3}$

e $\frac{7}{10}$ or $\frac{7}{9}$ **f** $\frac{5}{7}$ or $\frac{3}{4}$ **g** $\frac{5}{11}$ or $\frac{4}{9}$ **h** $\frac{4}{13}$ or $\frac{3}{5}$

6 By converting to decimals, find which number is larger in each pair.

a $\frac{4}{7}$ or $\frac{2}{3}$ **b** $\frac{8}{9}$ or $\frac{5}{6}$ **c** $\frac{3}{8}$ or $\frac{5}{11}$ **d** $\frac{7}{12}$ or $\frac{9}{14}$

7 Are these statements true or false?

a $\frac{2}{5} < \frac{3}{7}$ **b** $\frac{6}{11} > \frac{7}{10}$ **c** $\frac{36}{56} = \frac{27}{42}$ **d** $\frac{7}{8} > \frac{9}{10}$

6I Subtracting mixed numbers

Example

Calculate: $3\frac{4}{5}-2\frac{1}{3}$

$3\frac{4}{5}-2\frac{1}{3}=1\frac{4}{5}-\frac{1}{3}=1\frac{12}{15}-\frac{5}{15}=1\frac{7}{15}$

1 Calculate:

a $3\frac{5}{6}-2\frac{1}{2}$ **b** $6\frac{3}{4}-4\frac{2}{3}$ **c** $6-2\frac{2}{7}$ **d** $7\frac{1}{4}-3\frac{2}{3}$

2 A tank holds $15\frac{1}{2}$ litres of oil.

How much oil is left in the tank after $3\frac{9}{10}$ litres are removed?

3 Richard walks $15\frac{1}{4}$ km and Simone walks $9\frac{7}{10}$ km.

How much farther did Richard walk?

4 Work out.

a $5\frac{1}{6}+2\frac{3}{5}-1\frac{3}{4}$ **b** $10\frac{2}{5}-6\frac{1}{3}+3\frac{1}{2}$ **c** $4\frac{1}{6}-1\frac{5}{12}+2\frac{4}{5}$

5 Fill in the missing numbers.

a $\square+2\frac{1}{3}-3\frac{1}{5}=6\frac{2}{3}$ **b** $3\frac{2}{5}-\square+5\frac{3}{10}=7\frac{1}{5}$

6J–6M Multiplying and dividing fractions

Example

Calculate **a** $4 \times \frac{3}{5}$ **b** $6 \times 2\frac{2}{3}$ **c** $3 \surd \frac{4}{5}$ **d** $4 \surd 2\frac{1}{3}$

a $4 \times \frac{3}{5} = \frac{4}{1} \times \frac{3}{5} = \frac{12}{5} = 2\frac{2}{5}$

b $6 \times 2\frac{2}{3} = \frac{6}{1} \times \frac{8}{3} = \frac{48}{3} = 16$

c $3 \div \frac{4}{5} = 3 \times \frac{5}{4} = \frac{15}{4} = 3\frac{3}{4}$

d $4 \div 2\frac{1}{3} = 4 \div \frac{7}{3} = 4 \times \frac{3}{7} = \frac{12}{7} = 1\frac{5}{7}$

1 Calculate:

a $5 \times \frac{1}{5}$ **b** $6 \times \frac{1}{4}$ **c** $7 \times \frac{2}{3}$ **d** $3 \times \frac{4}{5}$

e $8 \times \frac{1}{6}$ **f** $2 \times \frac{4}{7}$ **g** $3 \times \frac{2}{3}$ **h** $4 \times \frac{5}{9}$

i $\frac{4}{5} \times 2$ **j** $\frac{5}{7} \times 3$ **k** $\frac{3}{4} \times 5$ **l** $\frac{2}{3} \times 9$

m $2 \times 3\frac{1}{2}$ **n** $3 \times 1\frac{1}{4}$ **o** $5 \times 2\frac{3}{4}$ **p** $4 \times 3\frac{2}{3}$

q $4\frac{3}{5} \times 2$ **r** $5\frac{4}{7} \times 3$ **s** $3 \times 4\frac{2}{9}$ **t** $7 \times 5\frac{3}{11}$

2 Work out:

a $\frac{2}{3}$ of 15 kg **b** $\frac{3}{4}$ of 20 m

c $\frac{4}{5}$ of \$30 **d** $\frac{7}{10}$ of 200 ml

3 Find $\frac{5}{8}$ of 3 days. Give your answer in days and hours.

4 Find the area of this rectangle.

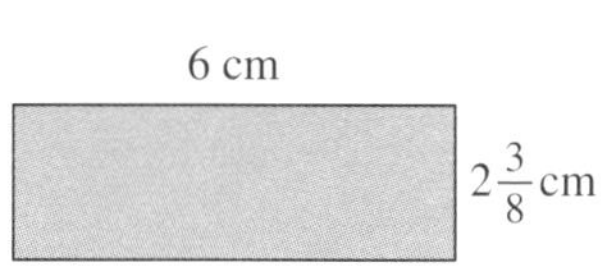

5 Copy and complete:

a $8 \div \frac{2}{3} = 8 \times \frac{3}{2} = \frac{24}{2} = \square$

b $8 \div \frac{4}{5} = 8 \times \frac{5}{4} = \frac{\square}{\square} = \square$

c $7 \div \frac{4}{5} = 7 \times \frac{5}{4} = \frac{\square}{\square} = \square$

d $5 \div 1\frac{1}{3} = 5 \div \frac{4}{3} = 5 \times \frac{3}{4} = \frac{\square}{\square} = \square$

6 Calculate:

a $3 \surd \frac{1}{4}$ **b** $7 \surd \frac{1}{2}$ **c** $6 \surd \frac{3}{4}$ **d** $8 \surd \frac{4}{5}$

e $6 \surd \frac{3}{8}$ **f** $8 \surd \frac{5}{6}$ **g** $5 \surd \frac{3}{10}$ **h** $6 \surd \frac{4}{5}$

i $9 \surd 1\frac{1}{2}$ **j** $5 \surd 2\frac{3}{4}$ **k** $4 \surd 1\frac{1}{3}$ **l** $8 \surd 2\frac{1}{4}$

m $10 \surd 3\frac{1}{2}$ **n** $8 \surd 3\frac{2}{3}$ **o** $9 \surd 1\frac{2}{7}$ **p** $11 \surd 3\frac{4}{5}$

7 A jug contains 8 litres of orange juice.
The jug is used to fill bottles that hold $\frac{2}{5}$ of a litre.
How many bottles can be filled?

8 Which is the better buy?

$\frac{2}{5}$ kg of chocolate for \$2.80

OR

$\frac{3}{8}$ kg of chocolate for \$2.70

7A Deriving formulae

Example

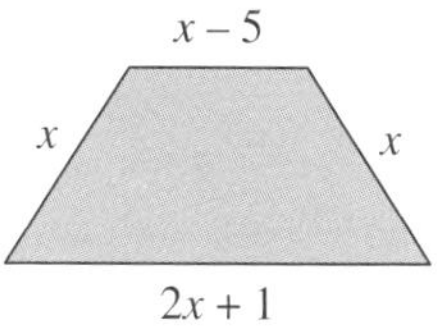

Derive a formula for the perimeter, P, of the trapezium.

Perimeter = sum of the lengths of the four edges

$P = x + x - 5 + x + 2x + 1$

$P = 5x - 4$

1 Karl has x stickers and Vicky has y stickers.
Derive a formula for each of these statements:

a Karl and Vicky have a total of 35 stickers.

b Karl has 15 more stickers than Vicky.

c Karl has twice as many stickers as Vicky.

2 The formula for converting degrees Celsius (°C) into degrees Fahrenheit (°F) is $F = \frac{9}{5}C + 32$.

Convert these temperatures to Fahrenheit:

a 10 °C

b 3 °C

c 25 °C

3 Derive a formula for:

a the perimeter, P, of the rectangle

b the area, A, of the rectangle.

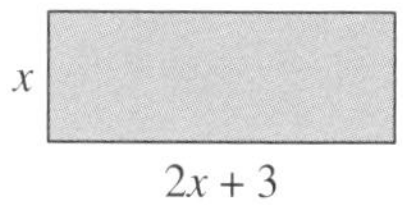

4 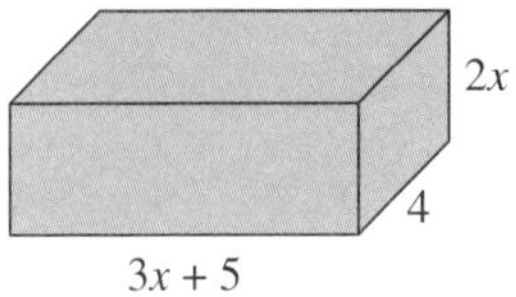

Write down a formula for:

a the volume, V, of the cuboid

b the surface area, A, of the cuboid.

5 Gregor starts with the number x.
He squares the number, multiplies by 2 and then subtracts 8.
His answer is y.

a Write down a formula connecting y and x.

b Use your formula from part **a** to find the values of x when $y = 90$.

7B–7F Deriving and solving equations

Example

Solve $5(x-2)=3(x+8)$

$5(x-2)=3(x+8)$	Expand brackets
$5x-10=3x+24$	Subtract $3x$ from both sides
$2x-10=24$	Add 10 to both sides
$2x=34$	Divide both sides by 2
$x=17$	

1 Solve:

a $2x+6=3$ **b** $3x+2=1$ **c** $7x+12=3$

d $14=2x+21$ **e** $20=3x+25$ **f** $15-2x=20$

g $15-3x=32$ **h** $30=18-5x$ **i** $27=14-2x$

2 Solve:

a $\frac{x}{2}-3=7$ **b** $\frac{x}{3}+2=5$ **c** $\frac{x}{4}-1=8$

d $\frac{x}{10}+7=9$ **e** $6-\frac{x}{3}=4$ **f** $8-\frac{x}{5}=2$

g $7=\frac{x}{2}+3$ **h** $10=14-\frac{x}{3}$ **i** $6=10-\frac{x}{2}$

3 Solve:

a $5x+3=4x+10$ **b** $4x-3=2x+9$ **c** $7x-8=5x-2$

d $5x-21=2x+3$ **e** $2x+3=15-2x$ **f** $2x+2=8-x$

g $7x-18=3x-2$ **h** $24-2x=3+x$

4 Solve:

a $3(x-2)=27$ **b** $6(x+4)=48$ **c** $2(3x-5)=38$

d $56=4(2x+3)$ **e** $16=2(3x+1)$ **f** $4(13-2x)=28$

g $\frac{x+5}{2}=7$ **h** $\frac{x-8}{3}=5$ **i** $\frac{2x-1}{4}=9$

5 Solve:

a $2(3x - 2) = 4(x + 7)$ **b** $5(x + 2) = 4(x + 9)$

c $7(x - 3) = 3(x - 1)$ **d** $3(2x + 6) = 4(x + 20)$

(e) $2(x + 3) + 3(x - 1) = 33$ **(f)** $7 + 2(x - 5) + x = 18$

6

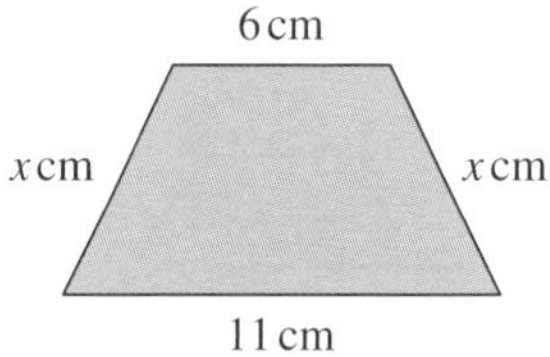

The perimeter of the isosceles trapezium is 32 cm.
Find the value of x.

7

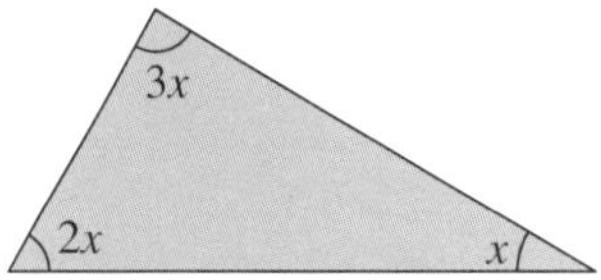

Find the value of x.

(8)

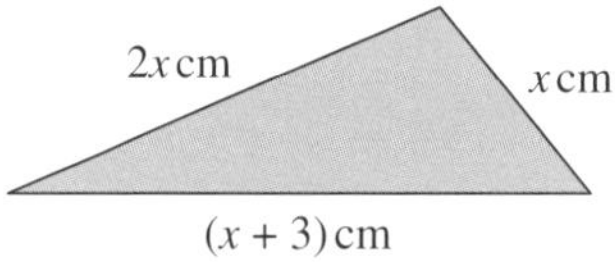

The perimeter of the triangle is 47 cm.
Find the value of x.

(9) The sum of three consecutive even numbers is 282.
Find the three numbers.

(10) Adam, Jason and Omar have a total of 71 sweets.
Adam has twice as many sweets as Jason.
Jason has 5 more sweets than Omar.

How many sweets does Omar have?

11 Using $A = 6x^2$, find A when:

a $x = 5$ **b** $x = {}^{-}3$ **c** $x = 0.5$

12 $I = 4Ft$

a Find I when $F = {}^{-}8$ and $t = 3$

b Find t when $I = 240$ and $F = 15$

13 $E = mgh$

a Find E when $m = 2$, $g = 10$ and $h = 5$

b Find m when $E = 420$, $g = 10$ and $h = 14$

14 $v = u + at$

a Find v when $u = {}^{-}5$, $a = 4$ and $t = 3$

b Find u when $v = 36$, $a = 2$ and $t = 6.5$

c Find a when $v = 18$, $u = 6$ and $t = 4$

d Find t when $v = 40$, $u = 13$ and $a = 4.5$

15 $a = \dfrac{v^2}{r}$

a Find a when $v = 8$ and $r = 16$

b Find v when $a = 25$ and $r = 16$

c Find r when $a = 10$ and $v = {}^{-}8$

16 $v^2 = u^2 + 2as$

Find u when $v = {}^{-}13$, $a = {}^{-}4$ and $s = {}^{-}15$

7G–7H Changing the subject of a formula

Example

Make r the subject of the formula $A = \pi r^2$.

The formula can be shown as a function machine:

$r \rightarrow$ [square] $\rightarrow$ [$\times \pi$] $\rightarrow A$

r can be found by reversing the function machine:

$r \leftarrow$ [$\sqrt{\square}$] $\leftarrow$ [$\div \pi$] $\leftarrow A$

which gives the formula:

$$r = \sqrt{\frac{A}{\pi}}$$

When you take the square root, the answer can be positive or negative, but in this case it is positive since r is a real-life distance.

1 Using function machines to help you, rearrange each formula to make the letter in brackets the subject.

a $b = ad + c^2$ (d) **b** $y = x + \sqrt{z}$ (z)

c $y = \dfrac{z}{x}$ (x) **d** $a = b + \dfrac{c}{d}$ (c)

e $m = \dfrac{1}{pqr}$ (r) **f** $a = \dfrac{bc}{def}$ (c)

2 Draw a function machine to show how to find:

a p, using $t = 7p - 50$ **b** b, using $P = 2(l + b)$ **c** h, using $A = \dfrac{bh}{2}$

3 Use the reverse function machine for each part of Question **2** to rewrite the formula. Make the letter you originally started with the subject.

4 $t \rightarrow$ [$\div s$] $\rightarrow$ [square] $\rightarrow R$

a Use this function machine to write down a formula with R as its subject.

b Use the reverse function machine to rewrite the formula with t as its subject.

5 In this question, take the positive square root, where appropriate.
Draw a function machine to show how to find:

a x, using $y = 3x^2$ **b** r, using $p^2 = q^2 + r^2$ **c** v, using $D = \dfrac{v^2}{252f}$

6 $\dfrac{a}{x} + \dfrac{b}{y} = 1$

Rearrange the formula so that the subject is:

a x **b** y **c** a **d** b

7I Inequalities

Example

Write down the inequalities represented by these number lines.

a

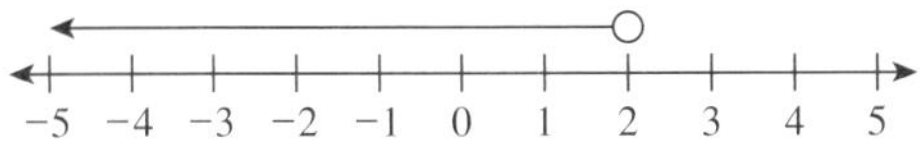

b

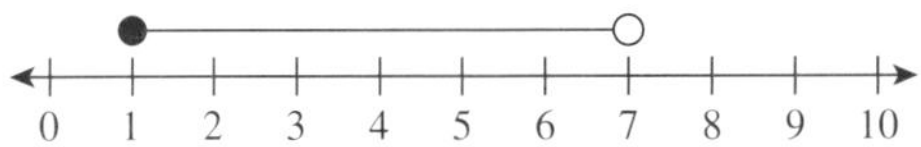

a $x < 2$ **b** $1 \leq x < 7$

1 Represent each of these inequalities on a number line.

a $x < 3$

b $x \geq 1$

c $x > -6$

d $2 < x \leq 8$

e $-3 \leq x < 2$

2 Write down the inequalities shown on these number lines.

a

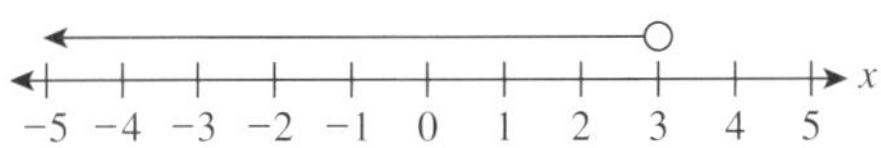

b

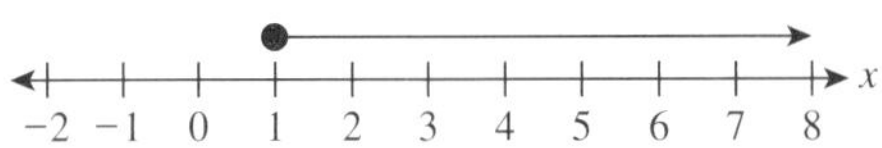

c

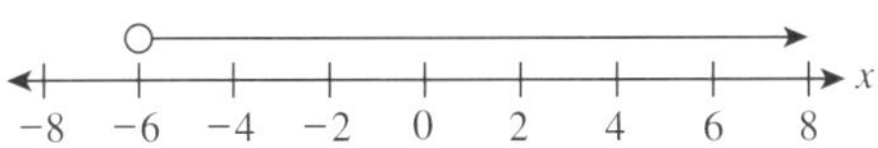

d

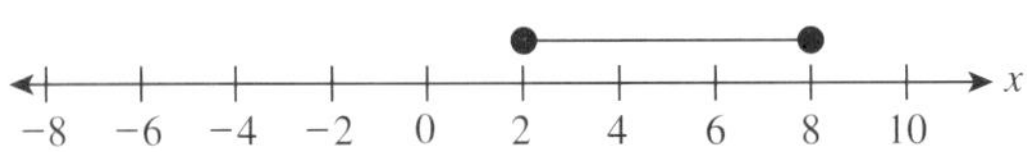

e

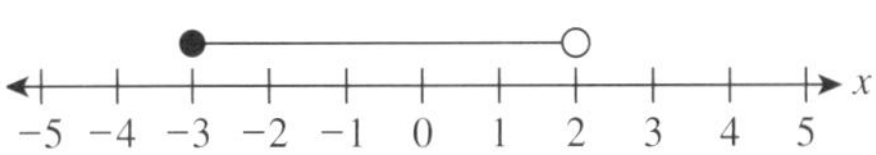

3 What is the largest integer that satisfies the inequality $x < 2$?

4 Write down all the integers that satisfy the inequality $5 \leq x < 9$

8A Exterior angle of a triangle

Example

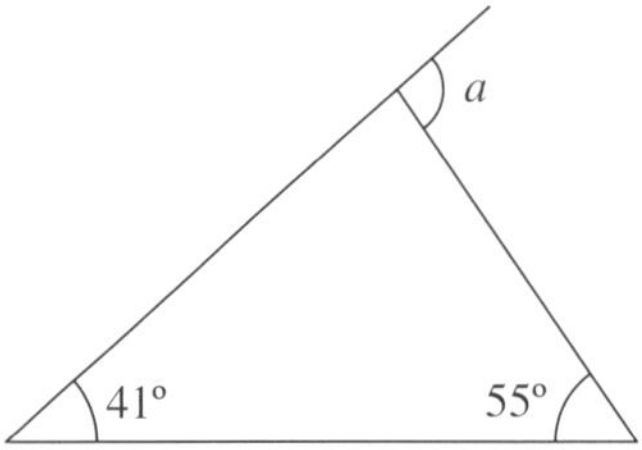

Find the value of angle a.

$a = 41 + 55 = 96°$
(exterior angle = sum of two opposite interior angles)

Find the missing angles.

1

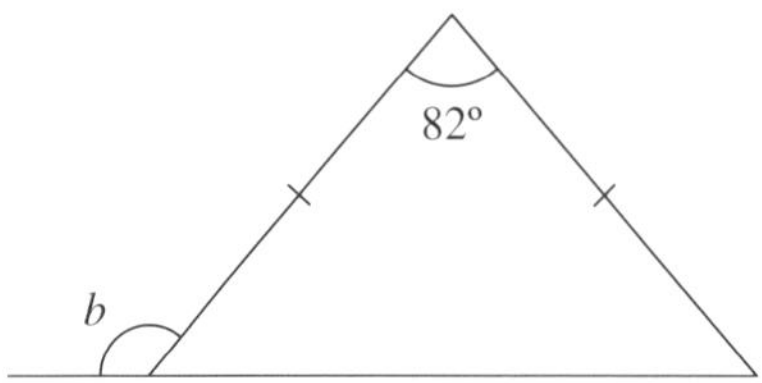

2

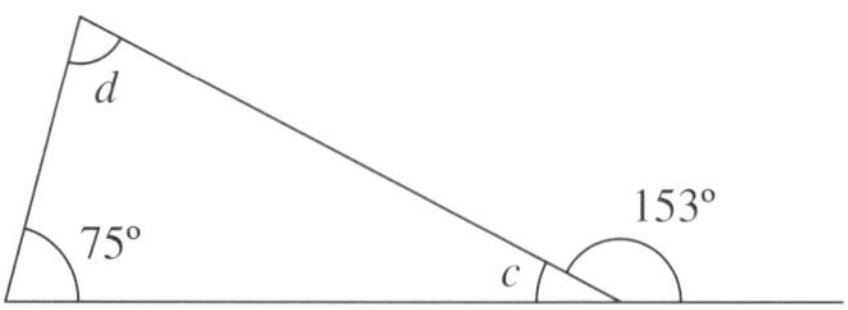

3

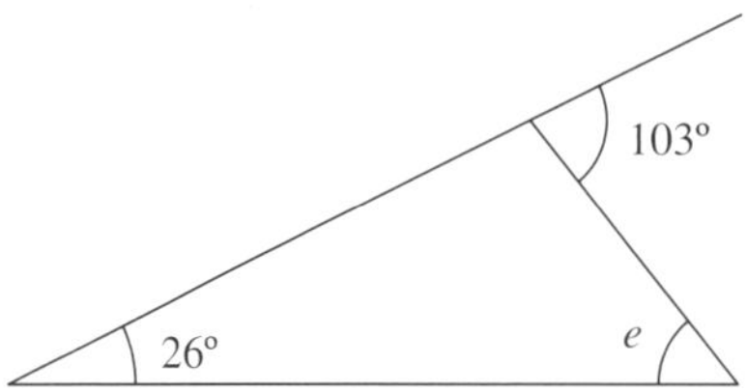

4

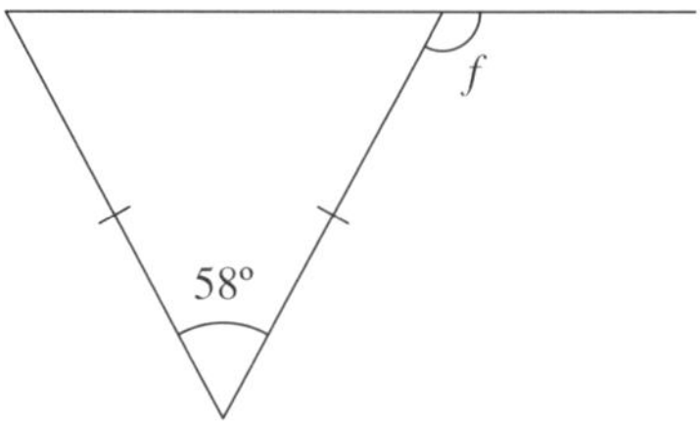

5 Find the size of each exterior angle for this triangle.

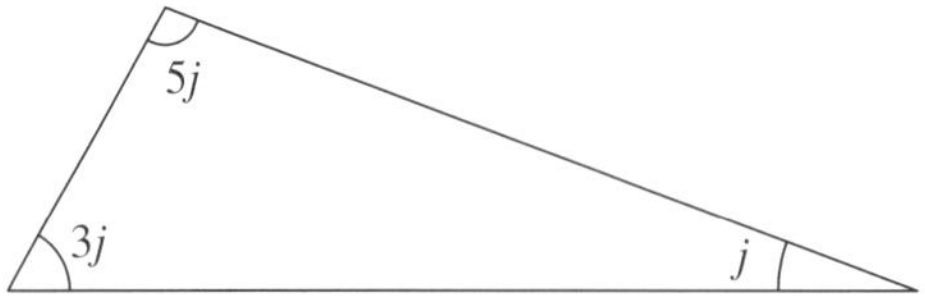

6 Find the size of the angle marked x in this diagram.

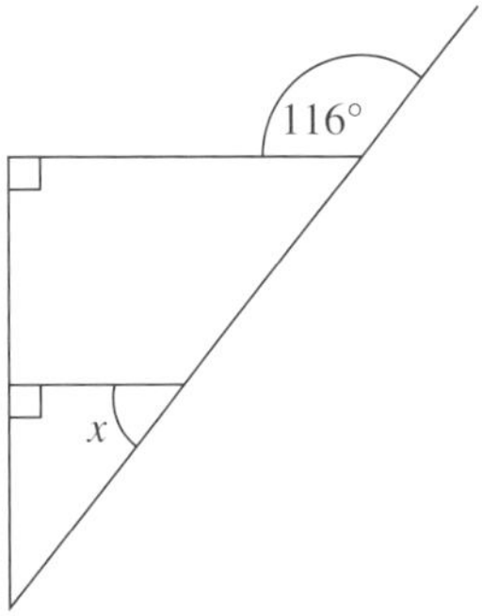

7 Write an equation in x and solve it to find the value of x.

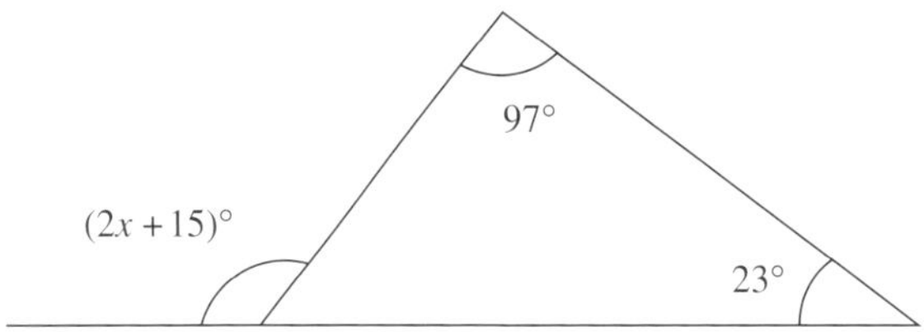

8B Angles in parallel lines and intersecting lines

Example

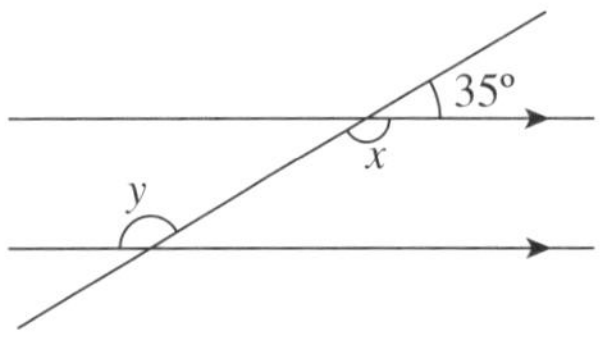

Find the values of angles x and y.

$x + 35° = 180°$ (angles on a straight line), so $x = 145°$

$y = x$ (alternate angles), so $y = 145°$

1 Find the sizes of the angles marked x and y.

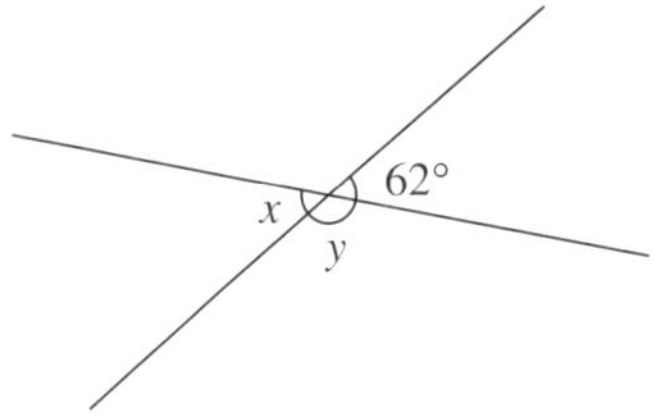

2 Calculate the size of each lettered angle.

a

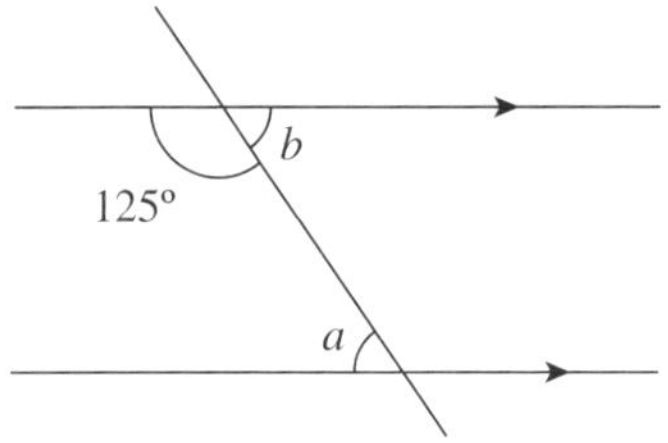

b

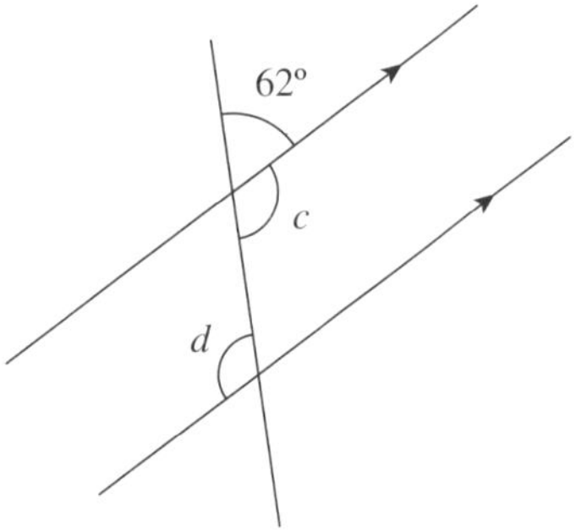

c

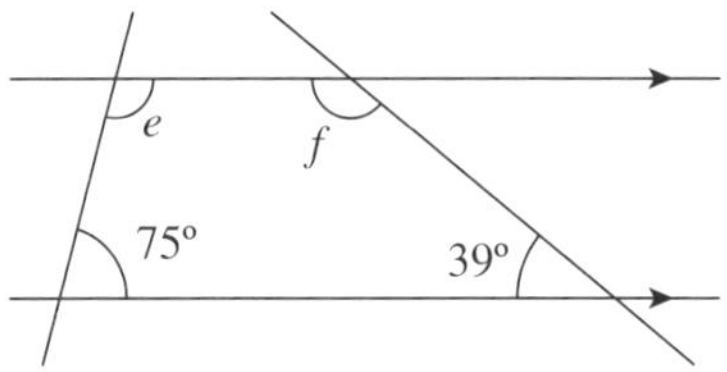

d

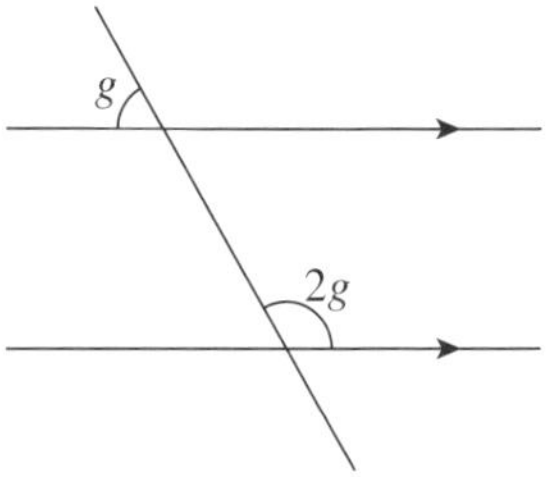

e

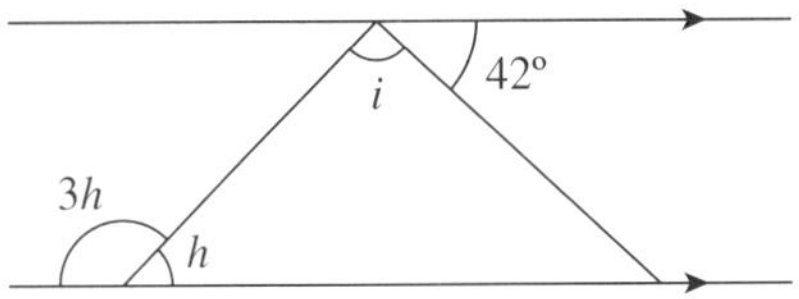

f

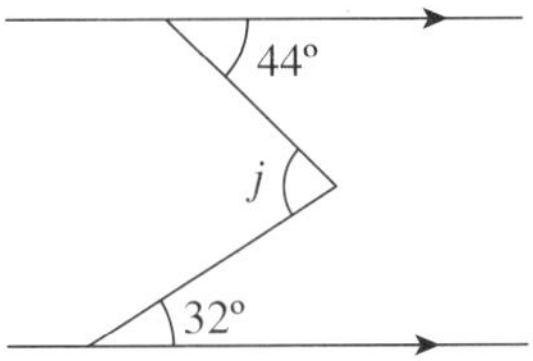

3 Find the sizes of the angles marked with letters.

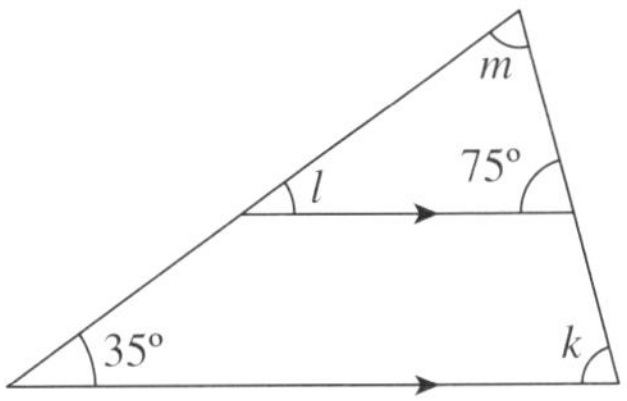

4 Find the sizes of the angles marked with letters.

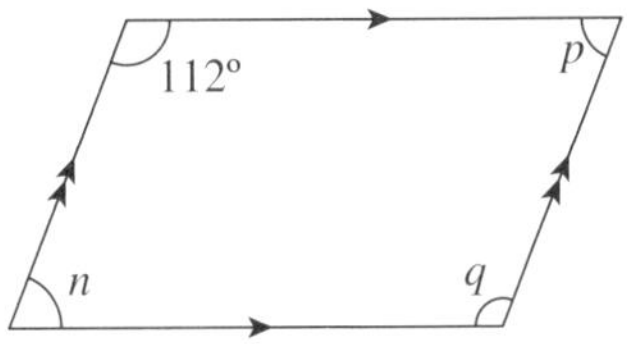

5 Saliha thinks that this quadrilateral is a parallelogram.

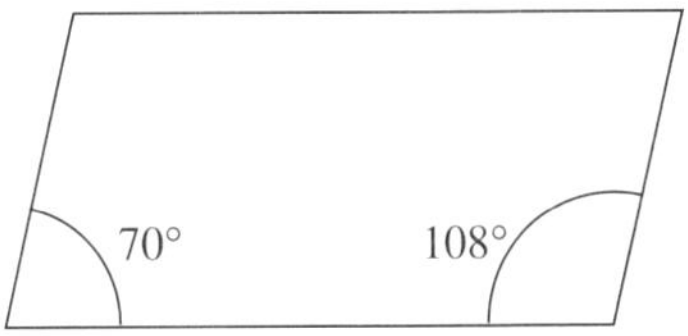

Is Saliha correct? Give a reason for your answer.

8C Midpoint of a line segment

Example

X is the point ($^-4, 4$) and Y is the point ($6, 1$).
Find the midpoint of the line segment XY.

The midpoint can be found using a grid:

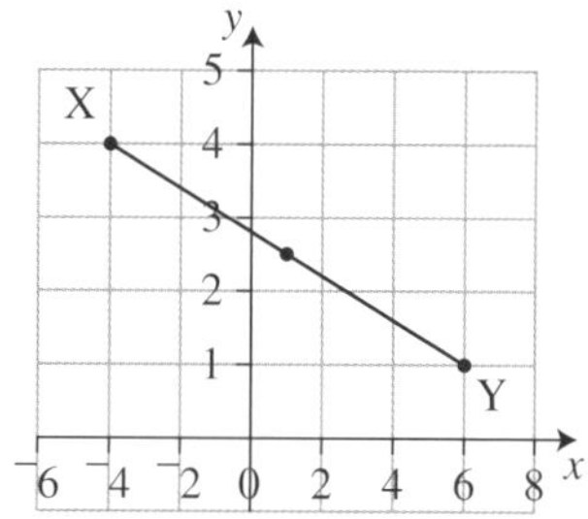

Midpoint = $(1, 2.5)$
The midpoint can also be calculated:
Midpoint =

$$\left(\frac{^-4+6}{2}, \frac{4+1}{2}\right) = \left(\frac{2}{2}, \frac{5}{2}\right) = (1, 2.5)$$

1 A is the point $(1, 3)$, B $(6, 2)$, C $(8, 5)$ and D $(3, 6)$.

a Draw the quadrilateral ABCD.

b What is the mathematical name for the quadrilateral?

c Measure angle ABC.

d Use your answer from part **c** to find the size of:

i angle BCD **ii** angle CDA **iii** angle DAC

e Write down the coordinates of the point where the diagonals AC and BD intersect.

2 Find the midpoint of the line segment joining these points.

a $(1, 1)$ and $(3, 5)$ **b** $(2, 0)$ and $(6, 6)$ **c** $(^-4, 2)$ and $(2, 4)$

d $(1, ^-2)$ and $(5, 0)$ **e** $(4, 3)$ and $(5, ^-2)$ **f** $(^-2, 6)$ and $(5, 1)$

3 M is the midpoint of the line segment AB.
M is the point $(^-3, 2)$ and A is the point $(^-5, 1)$.
Find the coordinates of B.

4 ABCD is a rhombus.
A = $(1, 0)$, B = $(6, 1)$ and M = $(4, 3)$

Find the coordinates of: **a** C **b** D

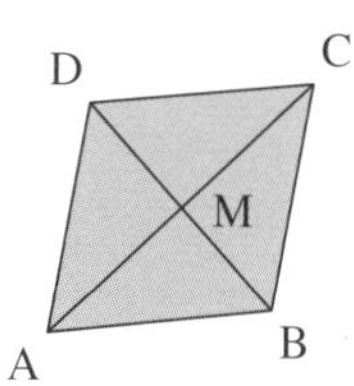

9A Multiplying by decimals

Example

Work out 2.4×0.3

Start by working out $24 \times 3 = 72$

so $2.\underline{4} \times 0.\underline{3} = 0.\underline{72}$

There are 2 decimal places in the product, so there must be 2 decimal places in the answer.

1 Work out:

a 2.6×10 **b** 15.83×10 **c** 0.04×10

d 5.045×100 **e** 4.7×1000 **f** 3.6×100

g 29.1×100 **h** 4.44×1000 **i** 0.06×1000

j 1.76×10 **k** 100×1654.3 **l** 1000×74.2

2 Work out:

a 0.3×9 **b** 0.8×7 **c** 3.3×6

d 5.7×4 **e** 9.6×3 **f** 7.8×8

g 4.1×11 **h** 0.6×12 **i** 3.45×12

3 A rod is 4.35 m long.
Find the total length of 8 of these rods.

4 Work out:

a 4.8×0.5 **b** 6.5×0.3 **c** 8.3×0.7

d 24.3×0.6 **e** 57.1×0.4 **f** 57.2×0.02

g 17.3×0.05 **h** 0.6×132.4 **i** 0.07×7.8

j 0.8^2 **k** 0.05^2 **l** 4.7^2

m $^-4.3 \times {^-5.4}$ **n** $8.2 \times {^-0.36}$ **o** $(-3.5)^2$

5 What is the cost of 18 cartons of juice, each costing \$1.85?

6 A tablet costs \$213.54.

What is the cost of 7 tablets?

7. A car has mass 1237.4 kg.

   What is the mass of 6 of these cars?

8. A square has a perimeter of 26 cm.

   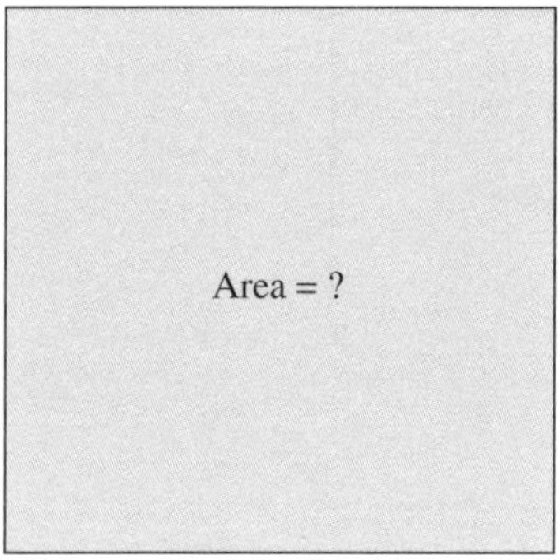

   Perimeter = 26 cm

   What is the area of this square?

9B Dividing by decimals

Example

Work out $3.54 \div 0.2$

$$3.54 \div 0.2 = \frac{3.54}{0.2}$$
$$= \frac{35.4}{2}$$
$$= 17.7$$

Multiply numerator and denominator by 10 to turn 0.2 into a whole number.

1 Work out:

a $28 \div 0.7$ **b** $6 \div 0.2$ **c** $6 \div 0.5$

d $24 \div 0.6$ **e** $4.5 \div 0.3$ **f** $9.6 \div 0.8$

g $18 \div 0.03$ **h** $3.2 \div 0.02$ **i** $84 \div 0.07$

j $2.25 \div 0.9$ **k** $2.68 \div 0.04$ **l** $60.2 \div 0.7$

2 Work out:

a $7.14 \div 2.1$ **b** $50.56 \div 3.2$ **c** $1.005 \div 1.5$

d $5.138 \div 0.14$ **e** $6.75 \div 0.25$ **f** $9.13 \div 0.83$

g $5.46 \div 1.3$ **h** $0.2184 \div 0.042$ **i** $0.01312 \div 0.16$

3 Work out:

a $^{-}53 \div 0.4$ **b** $^{-}43 \div 0.05$ **c** $^{-}71 \div 0.02$

d $^{-}94 \div 0.16$ **e** $^{-}85 \div 0.25$ **f** $^{-}99 \div 0.33$

4 1.2 kg of chocolate costs \$4.14.
Find the cost of:

a 1 kg of chocolate

b 0.8 kg of chocolate.

5

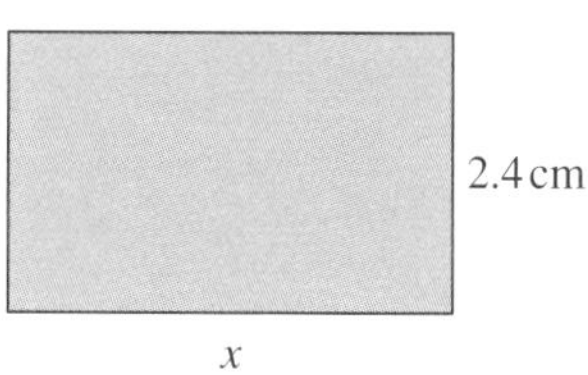

The rectangle has an area of $4.44\,\text{cm}^2$.
Find the length, x, of the rectangle.

6 The mass of an ant is 0.003 g.
How many ants have a total mass of 4125 g?

7 A plank of wood measures 12.54 m.

Pieces of wood 1.34 m long are cut from the plank.

How many complete pieces can be cut from the plank?

8 

A cheetah is timed moving 242.25 m in 8.5 seconds.

What is its speed in metres per second?

9C Percentage increase and decrease

Example

A train company increases its ticket prices by 8%.
Calculate the new price of a ticket that used to cost \$45.

An increase of 8% means 100% + 8% = 108% of the original value.
New price of ticket = 108% of \$45
= 1.08 × \$45
= \$48.60

Change 108% to a decimal, 1.08, and 'of' to '×'

1 Copy and complete these statements:

- **a** To increase a number by 40%, multiply the number by ☐.
- **b** To increase a number by 3%, multiply the number by ☐.
- **c** To increase a number by 6.5%, multiply the number by ☐.
- **d** To decrease a number by 24%, multiply the number by ☐.
- **e** To decrease a number by 8%, multiply the number by ☐.

2 Work out the new values:

- **a** Increase 300 kg by 35%
- **b** Increase 52 m by 8%
- **c** Increase \$76 by 5.5%
- **d** Decrease 90 km by 30%
- **e** Decrease 540 litres by 7%
- **f** Decrease 880 kg by 2.5%

3 Sunita is paid \$700 each week.
Her pay is increased by 12%.
Calculate her new weekly pay.

4 A new boat costs \$6500.
The boat depreciates (falls in value) by 22% in its first year.
Find the value of the boat after one year.

5 A dress costing \$150 is reduced by 15% in a sale.
Calculate the cost of the dress in the sale.

6 A laptop computer costs \$860 in 2020.

In 2021, the cost increases by 12%.

Calculate the cost of the laptop in 2021.

7 A pair of earrings is valued at \$540 in August.

In September, the value decreases by 18%.

Calculate the value of the earrings in September.

8 The population of a town at the start of 2019 is 85 000.

After 1 year, the population increases by 5.5%.

What is the population at the start of 2020?

9 \$12 000 is invested at the start of January. Each month the value increases by 8%.

How much is the investment worth at the start of March?

9D Simplifying calculations with fractions and decimals

Example

Calculate **a** $\frac{4}{7}+6\frac{5}{8}+\frac{3}{7}$ **b** $5\times 23\frac{2}{9}$

a $\frac{4}{7}+6\frac{5}{8}+\frac{3}{7}=\frac{4}{7}+\frac{3}{7}+6\frac{5}{8}=\frac{7}{7}+6\frac{5}{8}=1+6\frac{5}{8}=7\frac{5}{8}$

b $5\times 23\frac{2}{9}=5\times\left(23+\frac{2}{9}\right)=5\times 23+5\times\frac{2}{9}=115+\frac{10}{9}=115+1\frac{1}{9}=116\frac{1}{9}$

1 Use the laws of arithmetic to make these easier to work out:

a $\frac{2}{3}+1\frac{3}{4}+\frac{1}{3}$ **b** $\frac{5}{8}+4\frac{3}{11}+\frac{3}{8}$ **c** $\frac{7}{9}+5\frac{4}{11}+\frac{2}{9}$

d $\frac{3}{4}\times\frac{2}{5}\times 12$ **e** $18\times\frac{4}{5}\times\frac{2}{3}$ **f** $\frac{5}{14}\times\frac{5}{6}\times 28$

g $3\times 14\frac{1}{6}$ **h** $4\times 31\frac{3}{4}$ **i** $8\times 30\frac{2}{3}$

2 Work out:

a $5\times\left(\frac{2}{3}+\frac{1}{5}\right)$ **b** $\left(\frac{5}{9}-\frac{1}{2}\right)\times 4$ **c** $2\times\left(\frac{7}{8}-\frac{2}{7}\right)$

d $\left(\frac{1}{5}+\frac{1}{4}+\frac{1}{3}\right)\times 3$ **e** $\frac{8}{9}-\frac{2}{5}\times 2$ **f** $\frac{1}{4}\times 5+\frac{1}{3}$

g $\frac{3}{4}+\frac{1}{4}\times 2+\frac{3}{8}$ **h** $\frac{5}{6}-2\times\frac{1}{3}+\frac{1}{2}$ **i** $\left(\frac{4}{5}-\frac{1}{3}\right)\times\left(\frac{5}{8}-\frac{1}{2}+\frac{1}{5}\right)$

3 Work out:

a $\frac{3}{4}+2\times\frac{5}{8}$ **b** $\left(\frac{3}{4}+\frac{1}{3}\right)\times\left(5-\frac{1}{5}\right)$ **c** $2\frac{1}{2}+3\div\frac{2}{3}-\frac{1}{5}$

d $4\times 3\frac{1}{4}+5\div 1\frac{2}{3}$ **e** $8\div\left(1\frac{2}{3}+1\frac{1}{5}\right)$ **f** $3\times\left(\frac{3}{4}-\frac{1}{5}\right)+9$

g $3\times 2\frac{1}{4}-1\frac{1}{10}$ **h** $11\div 2\frac{1}{5}-2\times\frac{3}{8}$ **i** $\frac{1}{2}+\frac{2}{3}\times 9-5\div 1\frac{1}{4}$

10A Time series graphs

Example

The depth of water in a tank is measured every two hours.
The table shows the results.

Time	1 am	3 am	5 am	7 am	9 am	11 am
Depth (m)	1.4	1.1	0.3	0.8	0.9	1.2

Show this information on a line graph.
Use your graph to estimate when the depth of the water was 1 metre.

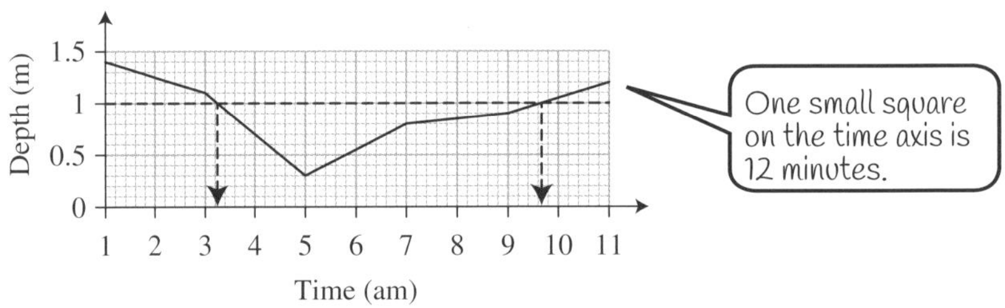

The water was at a depth of 1 metre at 3.15 am and at 9.40 am.

1 The temperature of a room was recorded every hour.
The table shows the results.

Time	1 pm	3 pm	5 pm	7 pm	9 pm	11 pm
Temperature (°C)	27	29	27	13	19	17

a Show this information on a line graph.

b Use your graph to estimate when the temperature was 14 °C.

c In which time interval did the greatest fall in temperature happen?

2 The table shows information about the depth of water in a reservoir.

	1 January	1 April	1 July	1 October
2010	30 m	27 m	21 m	10 m
2011	28 m	26 m	18 m	8 m
2012	29 m	28 m	24 m	12 m

a Show this information on a line graph.

b Comment on the shape of your graph.

10B Stem-and-leaf diagrams

Example

The stem-and-leaf diagram shows the ages of eleven people on a bus.

2	6 6 7
3	1 4 5 7 8
4	0 2 3

Key

2 | 6 means 26 years old

Find:

a the mode
b the median
c the range of these ages.

---

a The mode = 26 years old (because 26 occurs most often)
b The median = 35 years old (the sixth of the eleven numbers)
c The range = 43 – 26 = 17 years (the largest number – the smallest number)

1 The stem-and-leaf diagram shows the marks obtained by 24 students in a test.

2	1 4 5
3	2 3 3 4 6 8
4	0 0 0 2 2 4 4 5 6 7 8 8
5	1 5 9

Key

2 | 1 means 21 marks

Find:

a the mode **b** the median **c** the range

2 The data set shows the number of hours worked in a week by 20 adults.

51	43	62	41	54	37	47	52	66	41
38	47	57	34	43	51	65	41	39	58

Display the data on a stem-and-leaf diagram.

Find:

a the mode **b** the median **c** the range

3 The stem-and-leaf diagram shows the number of ice creams sold each day for a period of 20 days.

1	3 5 8 8
2	1 5 5 5 7 9 9
3	2 4 6 8 9
4	1 5 7 9

Key

3 | 1 means 31 ice creams

a Find:

i the mode

ii the median

iii the mean

iv the range

b The next day, 12 ice creams are sold. What effect does this extra value have on the mode, median, mean and range?

10C Histograms

Example

Mass (m kg)	$1 \leq m < 2$	$2 \leq m < 3$	$3 \leq m < 4$	$4 \leq m < 5$	$5 \leq m < 6$
Frequency	5	24	35	12	4

The table shows information about the mass, m, of 80 babies.
Draw a histogram to show this information.

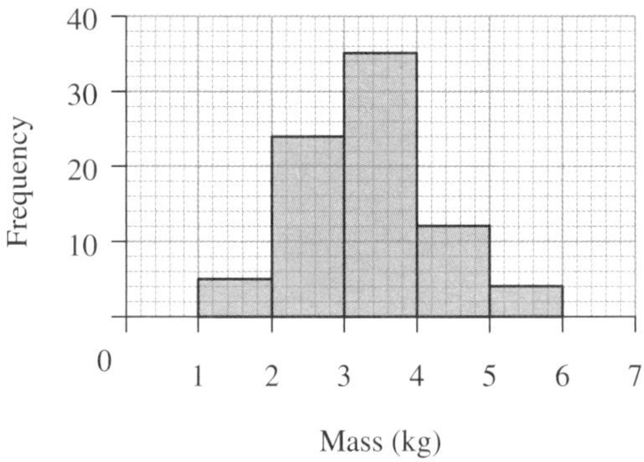

1 The table shows the speeds of 200 cars on a road.

Speed (v m/s)	$30 \leq v < 40$	$40 \leq v < 50$	$50 \leq v < 60$	$60 \leq v < 70$	$70 \leq v < 80$
Frequency	37	75	56	20	12

a Draw a histogram to show this information.

b Write down the modal class.

2 The data shows the height, h, in centimetres, of the students in Class 5A.

167	162	170	181	157	165	152	164
166	165	156	178	184	172	166	165
182	157	166	180	173	160	156	171
182	171	173	165	164	171	153	184

a Draw a grouped frequency table for the data.
Use class intervals $150 \leq h < 155$ cm, $155 \leq h < 160$ cm, …

b Draw a histogram to show the information in your table.

c Write down the modal class.

3 The times taken, in seconds, for students to complete a puzzle are shown.

12	15	19	32	18	27	36	8	19	18
31	22	41	45	56	26	28	29	31	33

a Avi drew this histogram for the data.

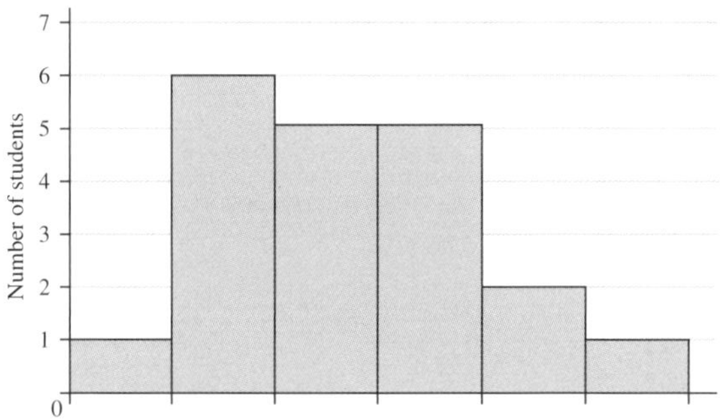

What class intervals did Avi use?

b Isabelle drew this histogram for the data.

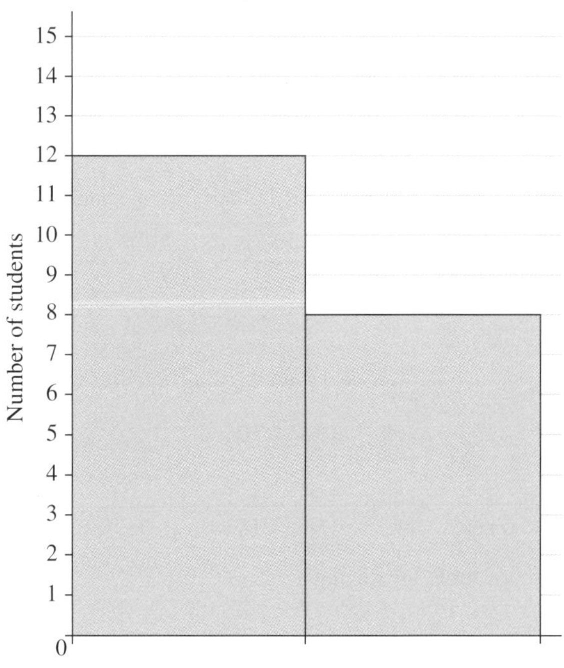

What class intervals did Isabelle use?

c Compare the two histograms. Which one do you think is better?

10D Interpreting and comparing data and diagrams

Example

The table shows Olga's and Fred's scores in 8 quiz competitions.

Olga	91	76	87	93	81	89	73	74
Fred	88	81	89	85	77	86	80	86

a Calculate the mean score for:

i Olga **ii** Fred

Comment on the results.

b Calculate the range for:

i Olga **ii** Fred

Comment on the results.

---

a i Olga's mean $= \frac{91+76+87+93+81+89+73+74}{8} = \frac{664}{8} = 83$

ii Fred's mean $= \frac{88+81+89+85+77+86+80+86}{8} = \frac{672}{8} = 84$

Fred's mean is slightly higher than Olga's mean, which means that on average Fred does slightly better than Olga in the quizzes.

b i Olga's range = 93 – 73 = 20

ii Fred's range = 89 – 77 = 12

Fred's range is significantly less than Olga's range which means that he is much more consistent.

1 The tables show the test marks of Class 8A and Class 8B.

Class 8A

17	21	28	43	24
37	32	45	38	29
30	23	17	24	39
24	34	26	33	19

Class 8B

31	12	21	30	27
38	43	28	33	31
23	36	47	49	37
35	24	31	27	31

a Show the information on two stem-and-leaf diagrams.
Compare your two diagrams.

b Calculate the mode, median, mean and range for both classes.
Compare the statistics that you have calculated.

2 A school conducts a survey of how the children and adults travel to school.

The results are shown in the pie charts.

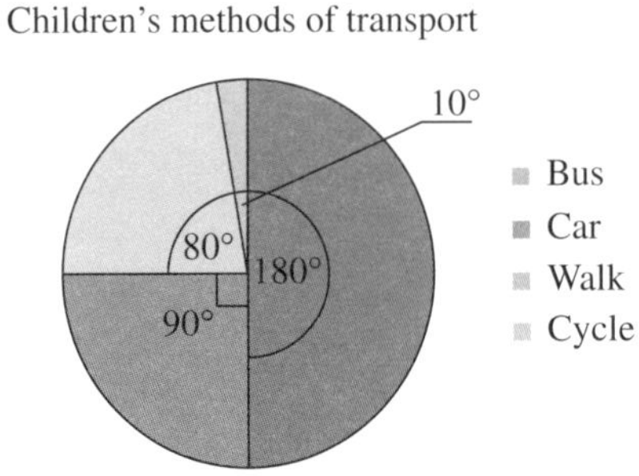

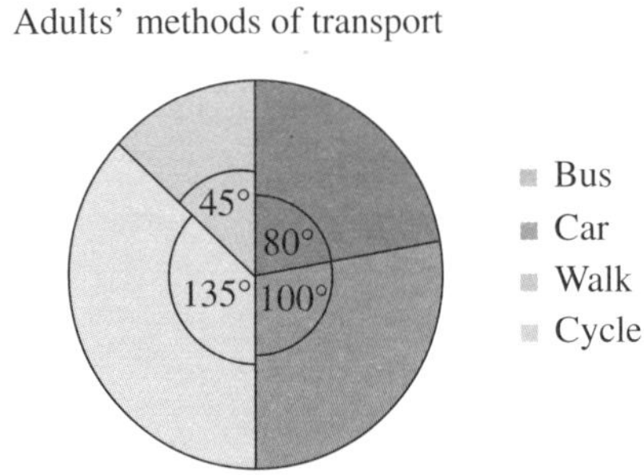

a A higher proportion of adults travelled by car to school. True or false?

b A smaller proportion of children cycled to school. True or false?

c Amrita says that more adults than children walked to school.

Is Amrita justified in making this claim? Explain your answer.

3 The time series graph shows the value, in $, of two paintings, A and B, over a period of six years.

a In which year did the two paintings have the same value?

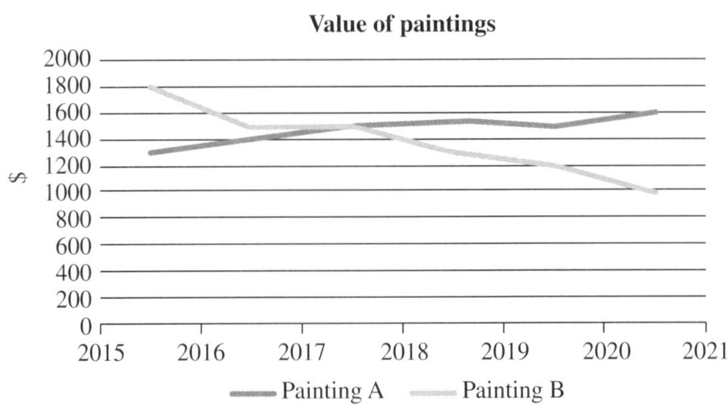

b In which year was there the greatest difference in value?

c Describe the trend in value for each painting.

d Nabeel says that by the end of 2025, painting B will be worthless.

Comment on Nabeel's claim.

11A–11B Rules of sequences

Example

The position-to-term rule for a sequence is *multiply by 3 then add 6*.
Write down the first five terms of the sequence.

1st term: $3 \times 1 + 6 = 9$
2nd term: $3 \times 2 + 6 = 12$
3rd term: $3 \times 3 + 6 = 15$
4th term: $3 \times 4 + 6 = 18$
5th term: $3 \times 5 + 6 = 21$

1 You have an unlimited supply of 2 cm and 7 cm rods.
What lengths can you make with them?

2 Find the next two terms in these sequences.

a 2, 6, 10, 14, … **b** $^-21, ^-18, ^-15, ^-12$, …

c 50, 47, 44, 41, … **d** $3, ^-4, ^-11, ^-18$, …

e 6, 12, 24, 48, … **f** 625, 125, 25, 5, …

3 Write down the term-to-term rule for each of the sequences in Question **2**.

4 Write down the 8th term for each of the sequences in Question **2**.

5 Find the missing numbers in these arithmetic sequences.

a 10, 13, □, □, 22, … **b** 7, □, □, □, 19, …

c □, 3, □, $^-11$, $^-18$, … **d** □, 14, □, □, □, 50, …

6 Write down the first five terms of these sequences.

a The position-to-term rule is *add 8*.

b The position-to-term rule is *subtract 4*.

c The position-to-term rule is *multiply by 2 then add 5*.

d The position-to-term rule is *multiply by 4 then subtract 7*.

7 The 9th and 11th terms in a linear sequence are 53 and 65.
Write down the first five terms of the sequence.

8 Find at least five solutions to each of these open-ended questions.

a Find two numbers that sum to 10.

b Find two numbers that have a product of 40.

c Find some numbers that have exactly six factors.

d Find some prime numbers between 50 and 100.

9 **a** Write down three different arithmetic sequences with a fourth term of 12.

b Write down three different arithmetic sequences with a common difference of 4.

11C–11D The *n*th term

Example

Write down an expression for the nth term of the sequence 9, 13, 17, 21, . . .

The common difference is 4 so the expression will contain $4n$.
The 'position zero' term is $9 - 4 = 5$.
So the nth term is $4n + 5$

Copy and complete these tables for each of the linear sequences. The first table has been done for you.

1

Position	1	2	3	4	5	6	20	n
Term	9	11	13	15	17	19	47	$2n + 7$

2

Position	1	2	3	4	5	6	20	n
Term	3	6	9	12				

3

Position	1	2	3	4	5	6	20	n
Term	5	8	11	14				

4

Position	1	2	3	4	5	6	20	n
Term	1	3	5	7				

5

Position	1	2	3	4	5	6	20	n
Term	7	11	15	19				

6

Position	1	2	3	4	5	6	20	n
Term	1	6	11	16				

7

Position	1	2	3	4	5	6	20	n
Term	11	17	23	29				

8

Position	1	2	3	4	5	6	20	n
Term	38	36	34	32				

9

Pattern 1 Pattern 2 Pattern 3

a Draw the next two patterns in the sequence.

b Copy and complete the table.

Pattern (*n*)	1	2	3	4	5
Black circles	2				
Grey circles	6				

c How many black circles are needed for pattern n?

d How many grey circles are needed for pattern n?

e Use your answers to parts **c** and **d** to find the nth term for the total number of circles in pattern n.

f If there are 60 black circles in a pattern, how many grey circles are there?

g If there are 75 grey circles in a pattern, how many black circles are there?

h If there is a total of 120 circles in a pattern, how many black circles are there?

12A Units of measurement

Example

a How many cm are there in 5.4 m?
b How many grams are there in 8.2 kg?

a $5.4 \times 100 = 540$ cm
b $8.2 \times 1000 = 8200$ g

1 Copy and complete:

a 0.58 m = □ cm
b 4 days = □ hours
c 240 minutes = □ hours
d 9000 kg = □ tonnes
e 7000 mm = □ cm
f 2.6 ℓ = □ ml
g 7800 g = □ kg
h 3.5 km = □ cm
i 2 days = □ minutes

2 How many 200 ml glasses can be filled using a 2.2 ℓ bottle of cola?

3 Copy and complete:

a 2 m^2 = □ cm^2
b 5 m^2 = □ mm^2
c 5.7 km^2 = □ m^2
d 5.2 m^3 = □ cm^3
e 9.1 cm^3 = □ mm^3
f 430 000 cm^2 = □ m^2
g 4600 cm^2 = □ m^2
h 7000 mm^3 = □ cm^3
i 32 000 000 cm^3 = □ m^3

12B–12C Simplifying ratios

Example

Write each ratio in its simplest form.

a 64 : 38 **b** 7 : 0.3 **c** $\frac{2}{5} : \frac{7}{10}$

---

a

64 : 38

÷ 2 ÷ 2

32 : 19

b

7 : 0.3

× 10 × 10

70 : 3

c

$\frac{2}{5} : \frac{7}{10}$

× 10 × 10

4 : 7

1 Write each ratio in its simplest form.

a 45 : 70 **b** 42 : 36 **c** 18 : 27 **d** 28 : 70

e 119 : 17 **f** 108 : 72 **g** 108 : 270 **h** 90 : 105

i 12 : 18 : 24 **j** 35 : 14 : 7 **k** 96 : 36 : 60 **l** 400 : 50 : 250

2 Write each ratio in its simplest form.

a 0.3 : 2 **b** 0.8 : 5 **c** 7 : 1.3 **d** 4.6 : 8.4

e 0.6 : 0.3 : 0.7 **f** 0.5 : 4 : 1.5 **g** 1.2 : 0.8 : 4 **h** 5.5 : 8 : 2.5

3 Write each ratio in its simplest form.

a $\frac{1}{2} : 6$ **b** $8 : \frac{1}{3}$ **c** $1.2 : \frac{1}{4}$

d $\frac{3}{5} : \frac{1}{2}$ **e** $0.8 : 15\% : \frac{1}{4}$ **f** $\frac{1}{2} : \frac{1}{3} : \frac{1}{4}$

4 **a** Which bag contains more flour: a bag containing 5 kg or a bag containing 500 g?

b Write down and simplify a ratio to compare the mass of the first bag with the mass of the second bag.

5 Use a ratio to compare these quantities.

a 50 cm, 1.3 m **b** 8 weeks, 4 days

c 500 g, 2 kg **d** 5 hours, 50 minutes

e 2.5 ℓ, 300 ml **f** 5.2 cm, 16 mm

g 3 minutes, 45 seconds **h** 6.4 tonnes, 880 kg

i 1 hour 15 minutes, 50 minutes

6 Use a ratio to compare these quantities.

a 4 cm^2, 4 m^2

b 2.6 cm^2, 54 mm^2

c 3 km^2, 500 m^2

d 2 m^3, 40 cm^3

e 1.4 cm^3, 25 mm^3

12D Sharing in a given ratio

Example

Share 96 sweets between Anna, Ben and Carl in the ratio 2 : 7 : 3

$2 + 7 + 3 = 12$ parts
1 part $= 96 \div 12 = 8$
Anna receives $2 \times 8 = 16$ sweets
Ben receives $7 \times 8 = 56$ sweets
Carl receives $3 \times 8 = 24$ sweets

1 Divide:

a \$120 in the ratio 2 : 1 **b** 750 cm in the ratio 2 : 3

c 3.42 kg in the ratio 1 : 2 **d** 48 minutes in the ratio 7 : 5

2 In this question, change the units to make the calculations easier. Divide:

a 2 hours in the ratio 9 : 1 **b** 2 weeks in the ratio 2 : 5

c 0.6 ℓ in the ratio 7 : 5 **d** 750 cm in the ratio 2 : 3

3 Share the following among A, B and C.

a \$102, in the ratio 1 : 2 : 3 **b** 90 kg, in the ratio 3 : 5 : 2

c 56 m, in the ratio 1 : 2 : 7 **d** 750 g, in the ratio 4 : 5 : 6

4 The three angles of a triangle are in the ratio 5 : 3 : 1. Work out the size of each angle.

5 **a** The three angles of a triangle are in the ratio 4 : 4 : 1. What type of triangle is it?

b What is the ratio of the angles in an equilateral triangle?

6 Find two numbers that are in the ratio 17 : 21 and have the sum 228.

12E Proportion

Example

Mike and Debbie invest money in a business in the ratio 4 : 3.
If Mike invests \$652, how much does Debbie invest?

\$652 ÷ 4 = \$163
Debbie invests 3 × \$163 = \$489

1 The ratio of adults to children on a train is 8 : 3.
There are 54 children on the train.
Find the total number of people on the train.

2 The ratio of male spectators to female spectators at a football match is 9 : 2.
There are 2565 male spectators.
Find the number of female spectators.

3 A length of string is cut into two pieces in the ratio 4 : 3.
The longer piece is 96 cm long.
Find the length of the shorter piece.

4 Jameelah is exactly 8 years older than Anna.
The ratio of their ages is 9 : 7.
How old is Anna?

5 An alloy is made of tin and zinc. 60% of the alloy is zinc.
What is the ratio of tin to zinc, in its simplest form?

6 A box contains blue and red pens. $\frac{2}{5}$ of the pens are red.
What is the ratio of blue pens to red pens in the box?

7 Two different types of pink paint are made by mixing red and white paint.

	Red	:	White
Paint A	2	:	7
Paint B	3	:	8

Compare these ratios to see which paint contains more red than white, and will therefore be the darker shade of pink.

8 A school is organising three trips to the zoo:

Mrs Vassieur is going on Monday with 45 students. The total cost will be $468.

Ms Omobkhe is going on Tuesday. The total cost will be $332.80.

Mr Redhaven is going on Wednesday with 25 students.

Assuming that the cost per student is the same for all three trips,

a how many students are going to the zoo on Tuesday?

b how much will Wednesday's trip cost?

13A–13B Translations

Example

The triangle ABC is mapped onto triangle A′B′C′ with vertices A′(⁻4, 2), B′(⁻1, 2), C′(⁻4, 4) under the translation

$\mathbf{T}=\begin{pmatrix} ^-5 \\ 1 \end{pmatrix}$.

Find the vertices of triangle ABC.

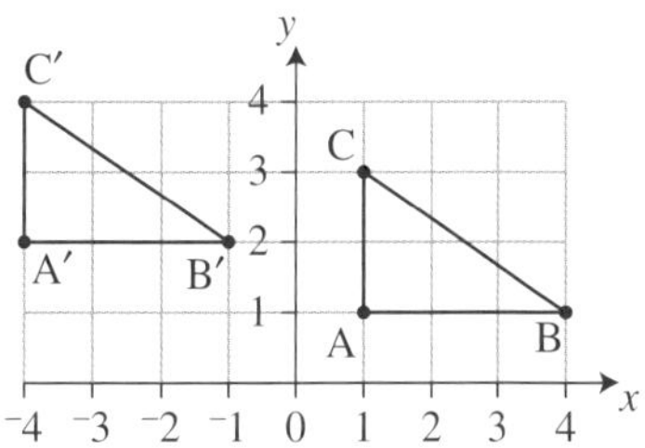

The translation $\mathbf{T}=\begin{pmatrix} ^-5 \\ 1 \end{pmatrix}$ maps ABC → A′B′C′.

So the inverse translation $\mathbf{T}^{-1}=\begin{pmatrix} 5 \\ -1 \end{pmatrix}$ will map A′B′C′ → ABC.

Thus A′(⁻4, 2) → A(1, 1)

B′(⁻1, 2) → A(4, 1)

C′(⁻4, 4) → A(1, 3)

So triangle ABC has vertices A(1, 1), B(4, 1), C(1, 3).

1 The vertices of trapezium ABCD are (3, 0), (4, 2), (6, 2) and (7, 0), respectively. Determine the vertices of the image trapezium A′B′C′D′ under the translation $\mathbf{T}=\begin{pmatrix} 4 \\ 2 \end{pmatrix}$.

2 The vector $\begin{pmatrix} 2 \\ 3 \end{pmatrix}$ maps triangle ABC to its image PQR.

Point A maps to P, as shown in the diagram.

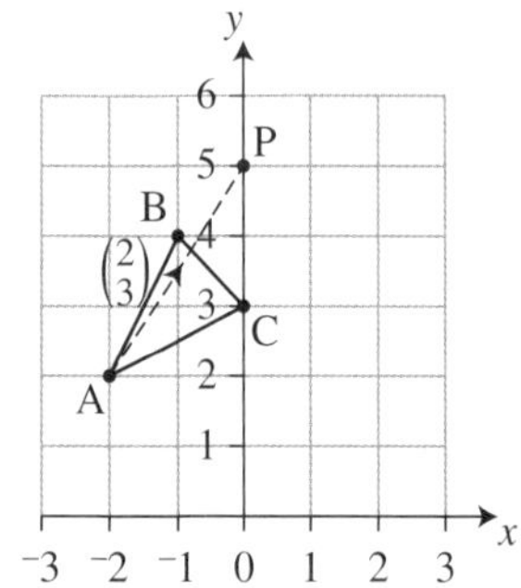

a What are the coordinates of A?

b What are the coordinates of P?

c Draw axes on squared paper for $x = {}^-3$ to $x = 6$ and $y = 0$ to $y = 7$. Mark triangles ABC and PQR.

A second translation maps triangle PQR to its image STU. The vector for this translation is $\begin{pmatrix} 2 \\ -1 \end{pmatrix}$.

d Show STU on your diagram.

e Write down the coordinates of S, T and U.

f What single vector maps ABC to STU?

3 Write down the translation which maps:

a X (1, 1) onto P (3, 2)

b X (1, 1) onto Q (2, ⁻1)

c X (1, 1) onto R (⁻2, 2)

d X (1, 1) onto S (⁻2, 1)

4 On squared paper, draw the kite ABCD with vertices A (2, 1), B (3, 4), C (2, 5) and D (1, 4). Translate ABCD with the vector **T**=$\begin{pmatrix} -2 \\ -1 \end{pmatrix}$. Label the image $A_1B_1C_1D_1$.

Then translate $A_1B_1C_1D_1$ using the vector **T**=$\begin{pmatrix} 4 \\ -2 \end{pmatrix}$.

Label this new image $A_2B_2C_2D_2$. State the vertices of $A_1B_1C_1D_1$ and $A_2B_2C_2D_2$. Give the vectors that translate:

a ABCD to $A_2B_2C_2D_2$

b $A_2B_2C_2D_2$ to ABCD

c $A_2B_2C_2D_2$ to $A_1B_1C_1D_1$.

13C Reflections

Example

S is a reflection in the line $x = 4$.
D is the quadrilateral with vertices $(1, 2)$, $(2, 1)$, $(3, 3)$ and $(2, 5)$.
Draw quadrilateral D on squared paper. Show **S**(D).

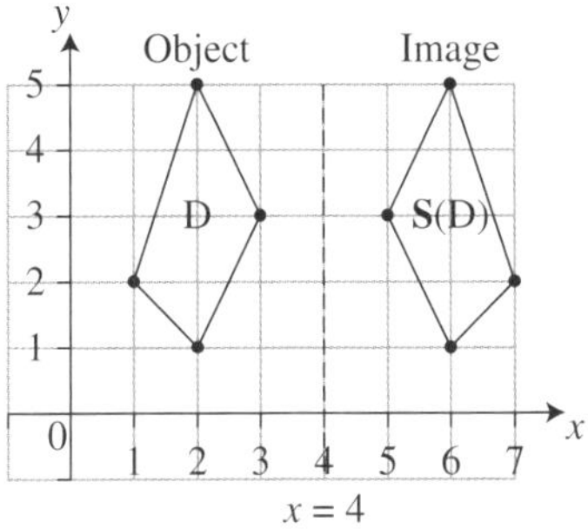

1

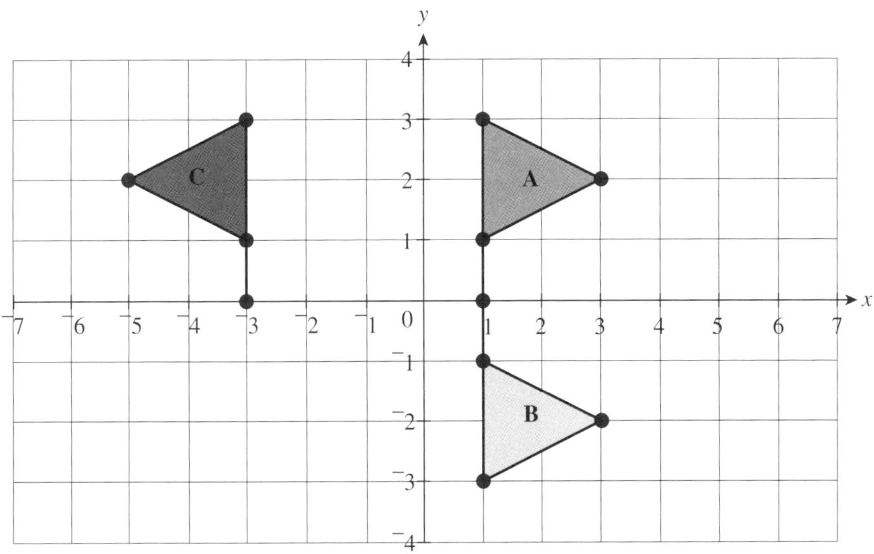

a Write down the equation of the mirror line that maps shape A onto shape B.

b Write down the equation of the mirror line that maps shape A onto shape C.

2 **M** is a reflection in the y-axis. L is the line joining $(1, 7)$ and $(2, 2)$.

a Draw the line L on squared paper.

b Draw **M**(L) by reflecting your line.

3 **R** is a reflection in the line $y = {}^{-}1$.
S is a reflection in the line $x = 1$.
K is the triangle with vertices $(1, 0)$, $(4, 1)$ and $(2, 1)$.

a Draw the triangle K on squared paper.

b Draw **R**(K).

c Draw **S**(K).

d Draw **RS**(K), by reflecting **S**(K).

e Draw **SR**(K), by reflecting **R**(K).

4 The table shows the coordinates of the vertices of a quadrilateral.
The quadrilateral is reflected in the line $x = 2$.

Vertex	Coordinates of image
(6, 4)	
(5, 1)	
(3, 2)	
(1, 7)	

Copy and complete the table by finding the coordinates of the image of each vertex of the quadrilateral.

5 A reflection maps the following points.

$(3, 1) \rightarrow (1, 3)$
$(4, 3) \rightarrow (3, 4)$
$(7, 3) \rightarrow (3, 7)$

What is the equation of the mirror line of the reflection?

13D Rotations

Example

The triangle with vertices at A $(1, ^-1)$, B $(2, ^-2)$ and C $(2, 1)$ is rotated through 90° clockwise about the centre $(1, 1)$. State the coordinates of the image vertices, A′, B′ and C′.

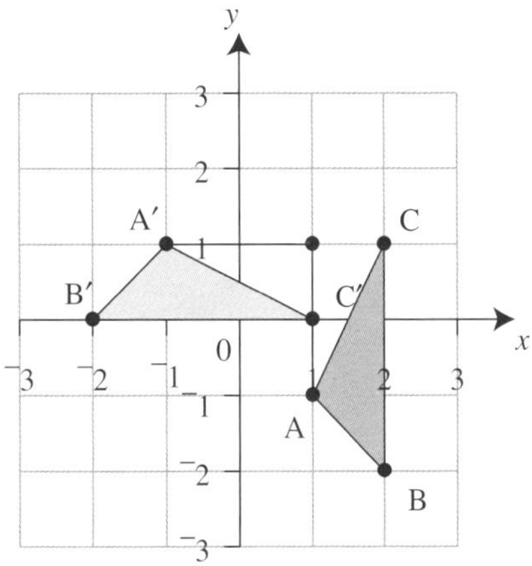

The vertices are A′$(^-1, 1)$, B′$(^-2, 0)$ and C′$(1, 0)$

You may use tracing paper throughout this exercise.

1 A triangle ABC has vertices A$(1, 0)$, B$(4, 2)$ and C$(2, 2)$.

a Draw triangle ABC on squared paper.

b Draw the image of triangle ABC after a rotation of:

i 90° clockwise, centre B

ii 180°, centre $(2, 1)$.

c Write down the coordinates of the vertices of each image of triangle ABC in part **b**.

2 **R** is a rotation of 90° anticlockwise about the origin.
Q is a rotation of 90° clockwise with centre (1, 0).
L is a rectangle whose vertices are (1, 1), (3, 1), (3, 2) and (1, 2).

a Draw rectangle L on squared paper.

b Draw **R**(L) by rotating L.

c Draw **Q**(L) by rotating L.

d What simple transformation maps **R**(L) onto **Q**(L)?

3 Describe the rotation that maps shape A onto shape B in each diagram.

a

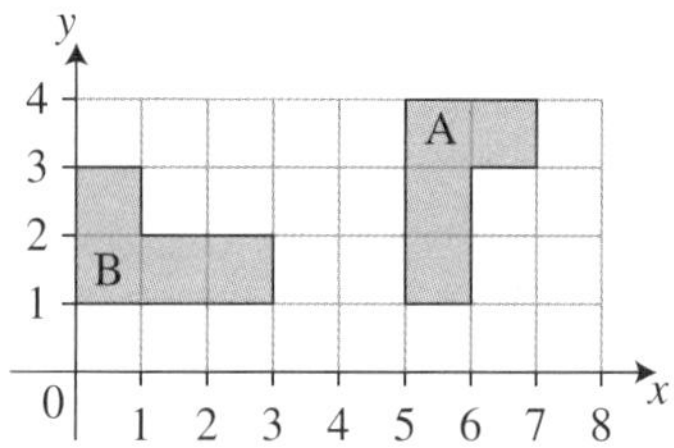

b

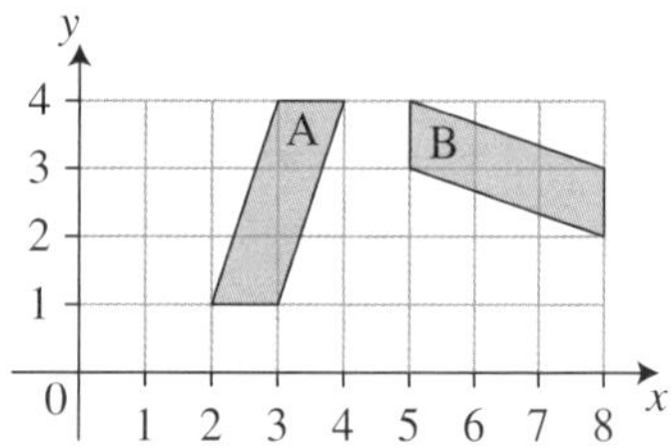

4 A quadrilateral ABCD has vertices A(4, 4), B(5, 6), C(9, 6) and D(9, 1). By drawing the quadrilateral, or otherwise, determine the coordinates of the image of ABCD after:

a a rotation of 180° about the origin

b a rotation of 90° clockwise about (1, 0)

13E–13F Symmetry

Example

Describe the symmetries of this shape.

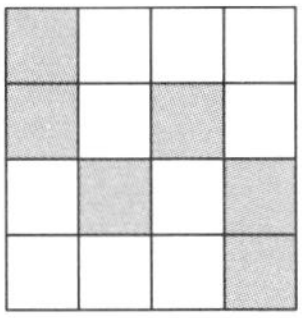

The shape has no lines of symmetry and it has rotational symmetry of order 2.

1 For each of these shapes, write down the number of lines of symmetry and the order of rotational symmetry.

a

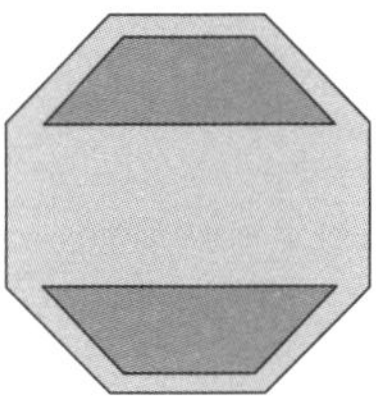

b

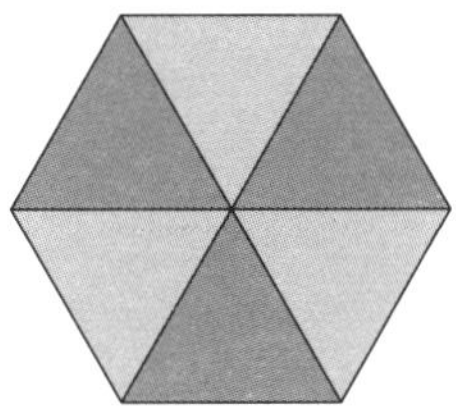

c

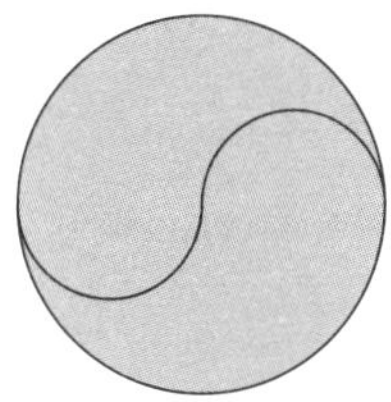

d

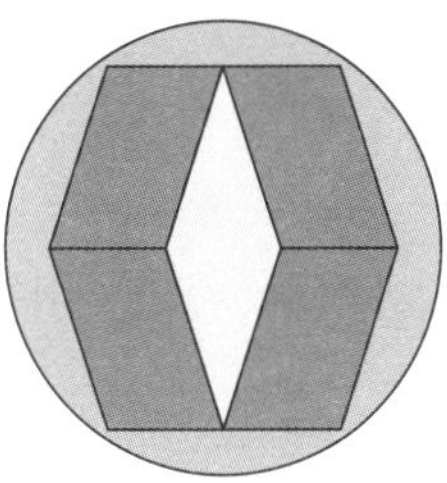

e

f

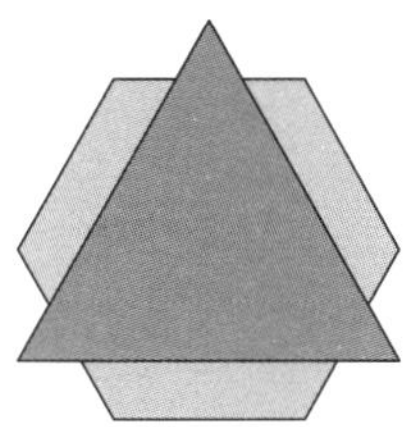

g

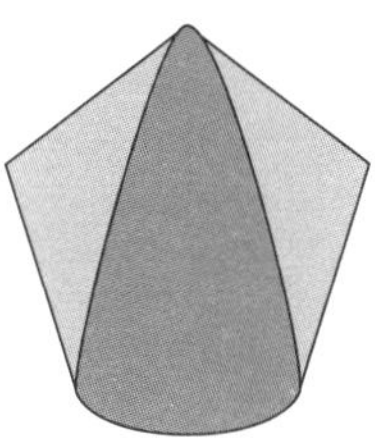

h

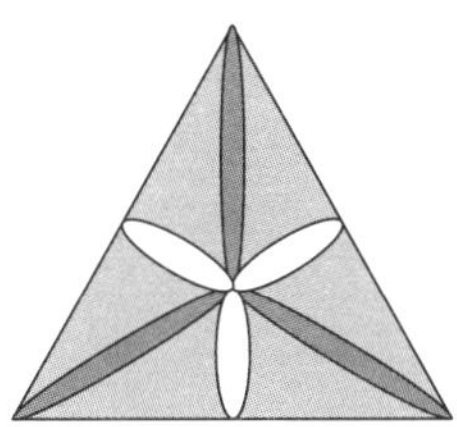

i

2 Copy the grid. Shade five squares so that the shape has rotational symmetry of order 2.

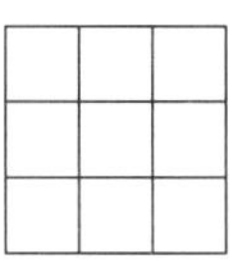

3 Half of each shape is drawn, together with its line of symmetry. Draw and complete each shape.

a

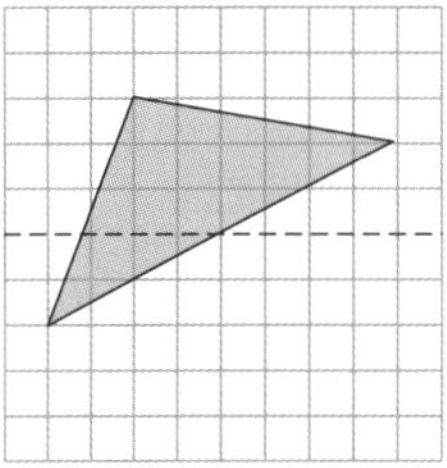

b

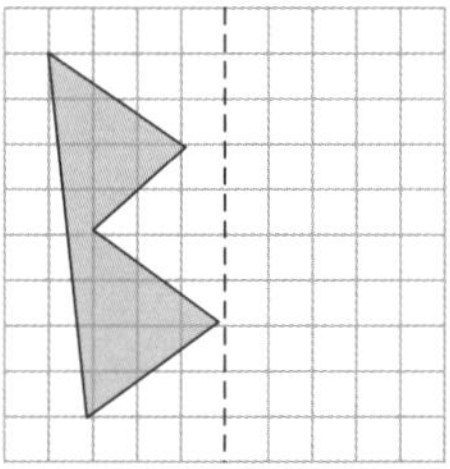

c

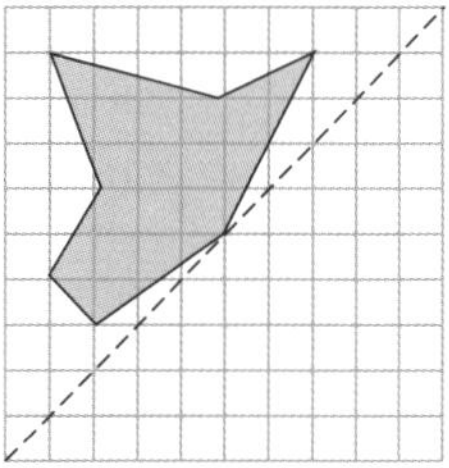

4 Write down the number of lines of symmetry and the order of rotational symmetry for each of these shapes.

a A rhombus

b A regular octagon

c A regular decagon

d An ellipse

13G Enlargements

Example

Find the image A′B′C′ of triangle ABC under an enlargement of scale factor 2 with centre of enlargement O (0, 0).

Join the vertices A, B, C of the triangle to the centre of enlargement, O. Extend OA to A′ so that OA′ = 2 × OA.

Repeat for OB′ and OC′.

The coordinates of the enlarged triangle are A′ (4, 4), B′ (12, 0) and C′ (8, ⁻2).

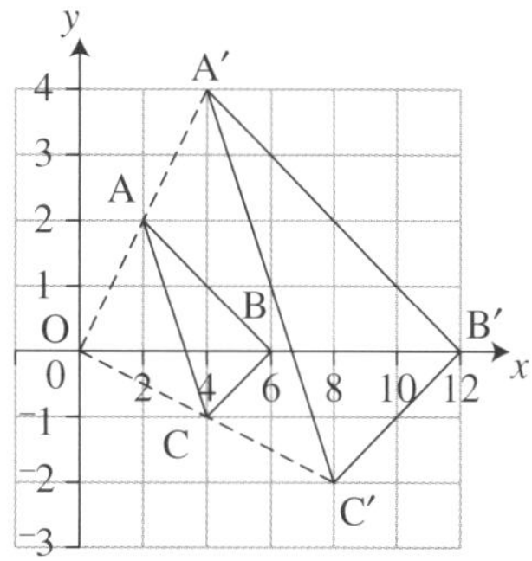

1 Copy the diagram. Draw an enlargement of the triangle with centre (0, 0) and a scale factor of:

a 3

b $\frac{1}{2}$

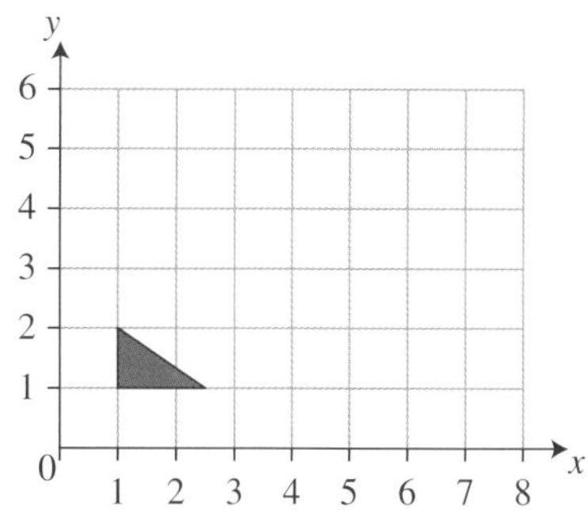

2 On squared paper, draw the triangles ABC and PQR with: A (3, 2), B (4, 2), C (3, 0) P (9, 4), Q (12, 4) and R (9, ⁻2).

a Is triangle PQR an enlargement of triangle ABC?

b Draw lines through AP, BQ and CR to find the centre of enlargement.

c What is the scale factor of the enlargement?

3 In the diagram, rectangle KLMN is an enlargement of rectangle ABCD with P as its centre.

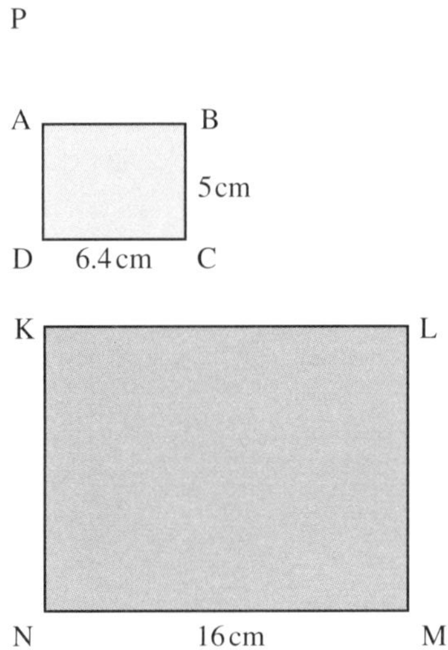

a What is the scale factor of enlargement?

b What is the length of LM?

c If PA = 4.5 cm, what is the length of PK?

14A Functions

Example

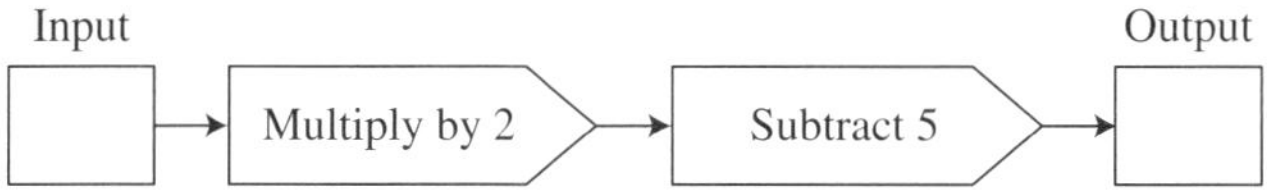

Find the output for this function machine when the input is:
a 17 **b** n

a Output: $2 \times 17 - 5 = 34 - 5 = 29$
b Output: $2n - 5$

1 For each mapping diagram:
i draw a function machine
ii write the output when the input is n.

a

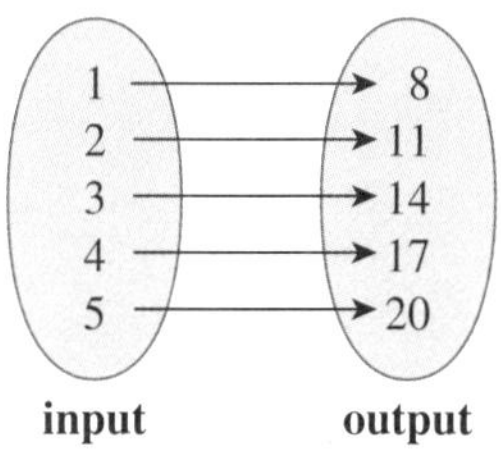

b

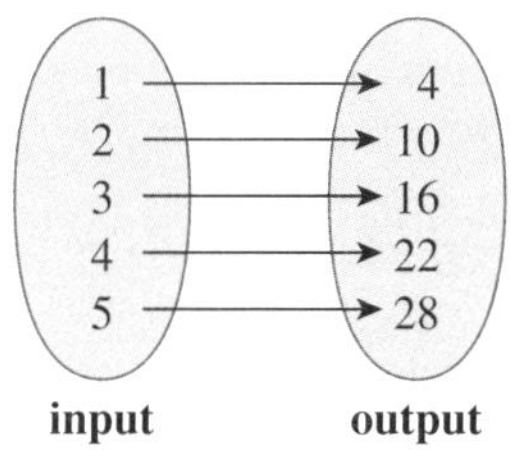

c

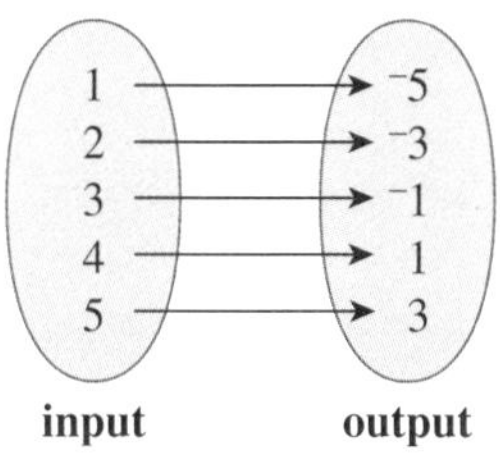

d

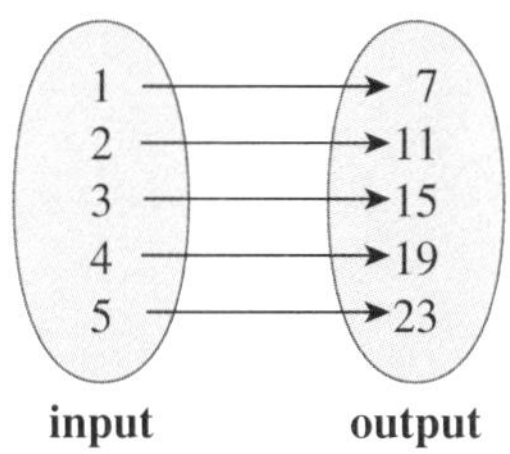

2 Copy and complete these mapping diagrams.

a

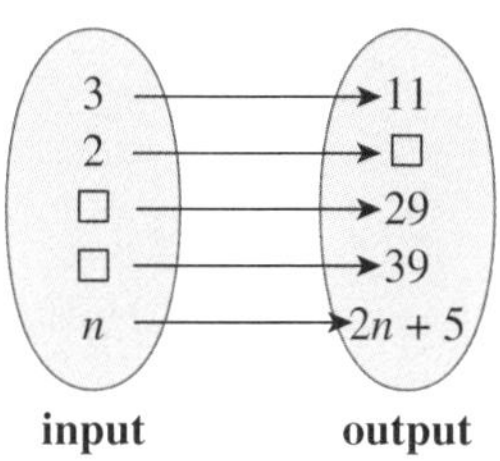

b

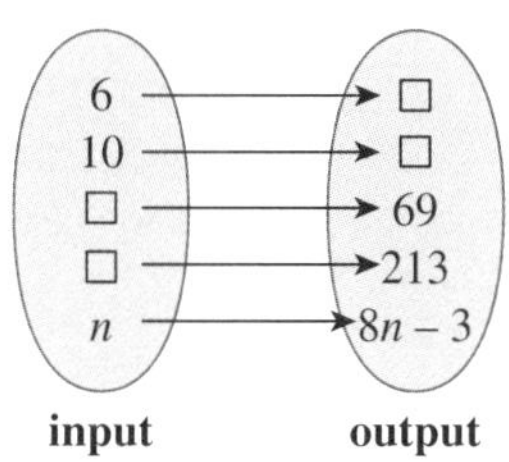

3 A function $y = 3x + 2$ can be represented by this mapping.

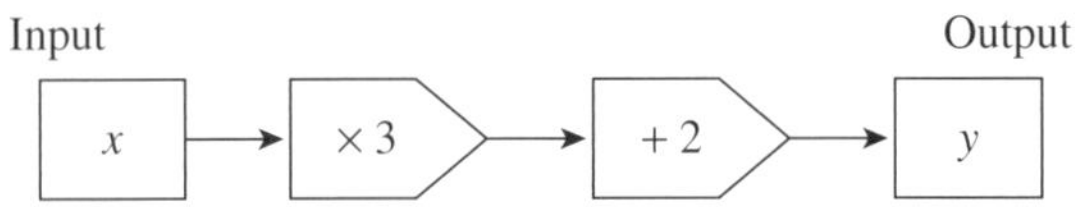

a Copy and complete the inverse function machine.

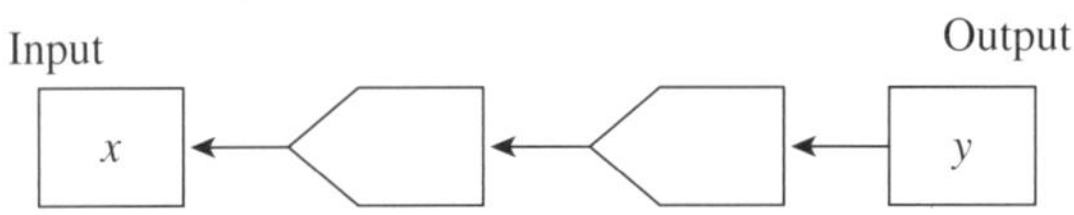

b Find the input x when the output $y = 11$.

c The input x and the output y are coordinates on the line $y = 3x + 2$.

Copy and complete these coordinates.

i (6, ________) **ii** (________, 17)

4 Draw function machines to represent these functions.

a $y = 2x + 1$ **b** $y = 4x - 3$ **c** $y = 0.5x - 5$

14B–14E Linear graphs

Example

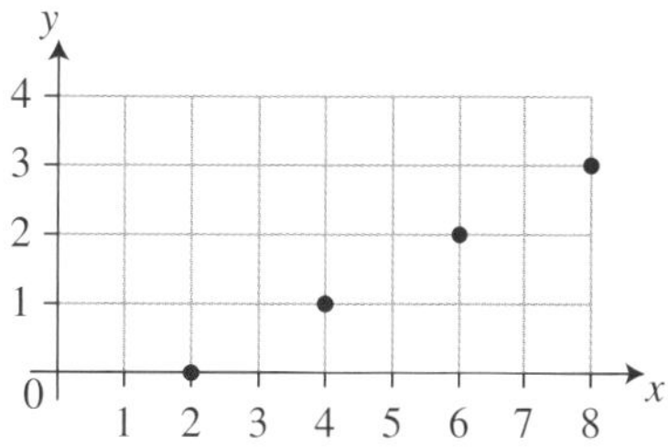

a List the set of coordinates shown.

b Write down the rule that has been used for the mapping.

a (2, 0), (4, 1), (6, 2), (8, 3)

b Divide the x number by 2 and then subtract 1 to get the y number.
The rule for the mapping is: $x \to \frac{1}{2}x - 1$

1 For the inputs 1, 2, 3, 4 and 5, draw a graph of the mapping of the x-coordinate to the y-coordinate using:

a $x \to x + 4$ **b** $x \to 2x + 5$ **c** $x \to 3x - 1$

d $x \to 3x$ **e** $x \to 2x - 4$ **f** $x \to \frac{1}{2}x + 1$

2 Using the inputs $^-2$, $^-1$, 0, 1 and 2, draw, on the same coordinate grid, graphs of the mapping of the x-coordinate to the y-coordinate using:

a $x \to x + 1$ **b** $x \to 2x + 1$ **c** $x \to 3x + 1$

What do you notice?

3 Using the inputs $^-2$, $^-1$, 0, 1 and 2, draw, on the same coordinate grid, graphs of the mapping of the x-coordinate to the y-coordinate using:

a $x \to 3x - 2$ **b** $x \to 3x + 1$ **c** $x \to 3x + 2$

What do you notice?

4 For each of the following, copy and complete the table and then draw a graph of the function.

x	0	2	4
y			

a $y = x + 2$ **b** $y = 2x - 2$ **c** $y = \frac{1}{2}x + 1$

d $y = 3x - 2$ **e** $y = \frac{1}{2}x - 2$ **f** $y = 3x + 5$

5 Which of these points lie on the line $y = 8 - 2x$?

$(^-2, 4)$ $(3, 2)$ $(5, ^-2)$ $(0, 6)$

6 Plot these graphs on the same set of axes:

$y = 3x - 4$ $y = 2x - 1$

Write down the coordinates of the point where the two lines intersect.

7 Plot these graphs on the same set of axes:

$y = 2x$ $y = 2x + 3$ $y = 2x - 1$

What do you notice?

8 Write each of these equations (where necessary) in the form $y = mx + c$ and then write down the values of: **i** m **ii** c

a $y = 2x + 4$

b $y = 5x - 8$

c $y = \frac{1}{2}x + 8$

d $y = x + 3$

e $y = 5x$

f $y = 7$

g $y = 6 + 2x$

h $y = 5 + x$

i $y = 8 - 3x$

j $y = 3 - \frac{1}{2}x$

k $2y = 4x + 6$

l $2x + y = 10$

9 Which of these are straight lines?

$y = 3 - 2x$ $xy = 12$ $y = 5$ $y = x^2 + 2$

$y = \frac{6}{x} + 1$ $y = {}^-2x$ $y = x^2 + 5x + 4$ $y = \frac{1}{2}x + 9$

10 For each of these straight lines, write down five points that lie on the line and work out the equation of the line.

a

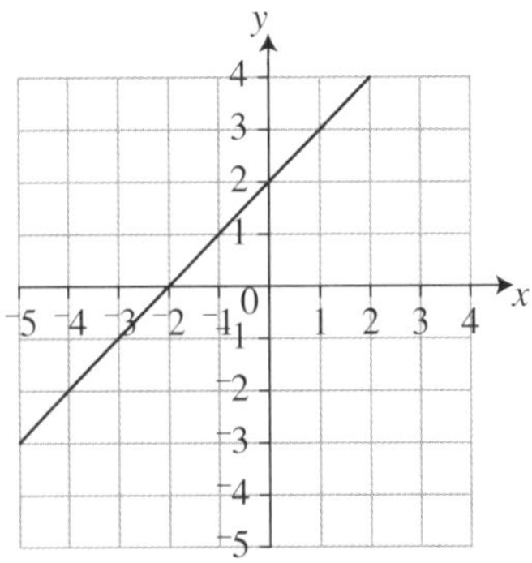

b

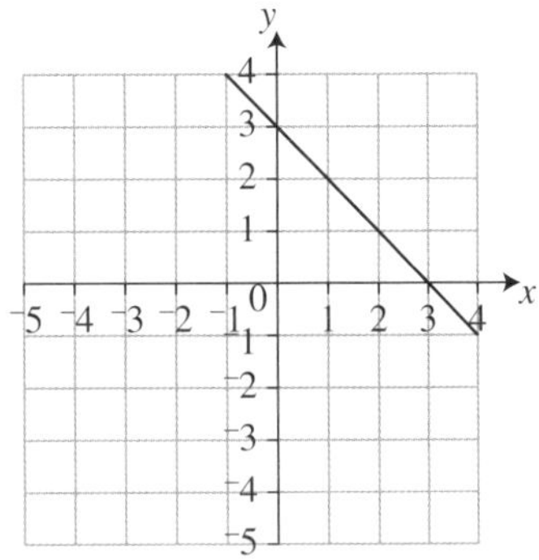

14F–14G Real-life graphs

Example

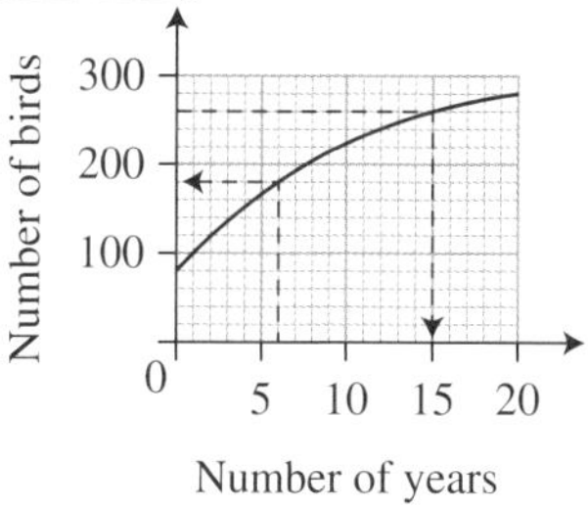

The graph shows how the number of birds on an island is expected to increase over the next 20 years.
Use the graph to estimate how many:

a birds there will be after 6 years

b years it will take for there to be 260 birds.

---

a 180 birds **b** 15 years

1

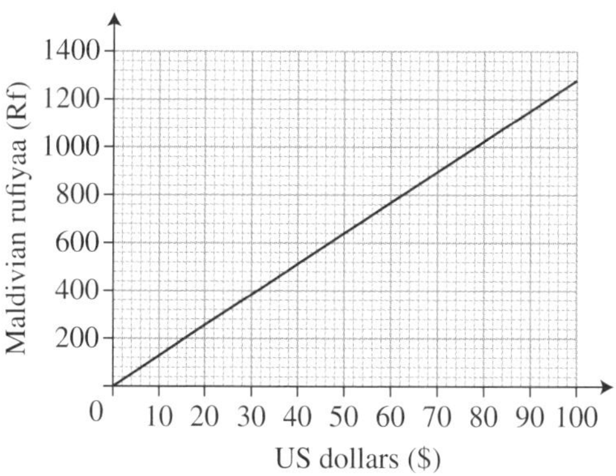

The graph can be used to convert between US dollars ($) and Maldivian rufiyaa (Rf).

a Use the graph to convert these amounts in dollars into Maldivian rufiyaa.

i $50 **ii** $74 **iii** $25 **iv** $88

b Use the graph to convert these amounts in Maldivian rufiyaa into dollars.

i Rf 200 **ii** Rf 700 **iii** Rf 880 **iv** Rf 360

2 The table shows the speed of a runner during the first 12 seconds of a race.

Time (sec)	0	2	4	6	8	10	12
Speed (m/s)	0	4	6.2	7.4	7.8	7.9	8

a Draw a graph to show this information.
Use a scale of 1 cm to 1 second on the horizontal axis and 1 cm to 1 m/s on the vertical axis.

b Use your graph to find the speed after:

i 1.4 s **ii** 4.8 s

c Use your graph to find the time taken for the speed to reach:

i 2 m/s **ii** 4.2 m/s

3 The table shows the temperature of a cup of tea as it cools down.

Time (min)	0	5	10	15	20	25	35	40	45
Temperature (°C)	85	70	61	53	46	40	30	25	24

a Draw a graph to show this information. Use a scale of 1 cm to 5 min on the horizontal axis and a scale of 1 cm to 10 °C on the vertical axis.

b Use your graph to find the temperature after:

i 12 min **ii** 24 min

c Use your graph to find the time taken for the temperature to cool to:

i 60 °C **ii** 36 °C

4 The graph shows information about Jim's (J) and Sue's (S) journey of 150 km along a road from town *A* to town *B*.

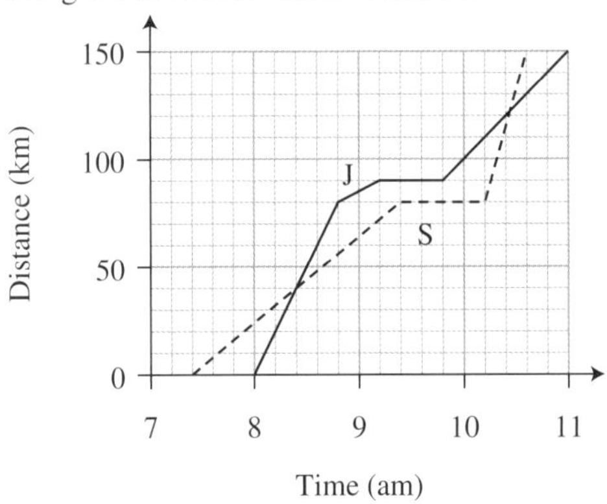

a What time did: **i** Jim leave town *A* **ii** Sue leave town *A*?

b What time did: **i** Jim arrive at town *B* **ii** Sue arrive at town *B*?

c How long did: **i** Jim stop **ii** Sue stop?

d At what time did: **i** Jim pass Sue **ii** Sue pass Jim?

e Calculate Jim's average speed for the whole journey.

15A Experimental probability

Example

The table shows the results when a six-sided dice is thrown 30 times.

Score	1	2	3	4	5	6
Frequency	8	3	7	4	6	2

Use the results from the table to write down the probability of throwing:

a a 5 **b** a number greater than 3.

a $P(5) = \frac{6}{30} = \frac{1}{5}$ **b** $P(\text{number} > 3) = \frac{4+6+2}{30} = \frac{12}{30} = \frac{2}{5}$

1 Assign a probability from 0 to 1 to each event.

a You will increase in mass by 20 kg in the next 5 seconds.

b You will blink in the next 24 hours.

c A letter chosen at random from the word CERTAIN will be a T.

2 There are 15 females and 25 males on a bus.
Write down the probability that a person chosen randomly from the bus will be:

a female **b** male

3 The table shows the results when a four-sided dice is thrown 50 times.

Score	1	2	3	4
Frequency	8	20	13	9

Use the results from the table to write down the probability of throwing:

a a 1 **b** an odd number **c** a number less than 3

d a prime number **e** a factor of 12 **f** a number greater than 5.

4 The bar chart shows how students in Class 8A travel to school.

a How many students are in Class 8A?

b Write down the probability that a student:

i cycles to school

ii does not walk to school.

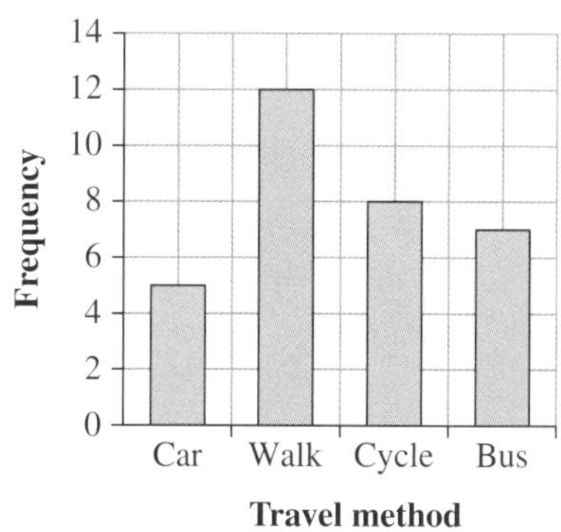

15B–15C Theoretical probability

Example

There are 5 red and 3 blue pencils in a box.
A pencil is selected at random.
Write down the probability that the pencil is:

a red **b** blue **c** pink.

a $P(\text{red}) = \frac{5}{8}$ **b** $P(\text{blue}) = \frac{3}{8}$ **c** $P(\text{pink}) = \frac{0}{8} = 0$

1 A letter is chosen at random from the word PARALLELOGRAM.
Write down the probability that it is the letter:

a P **b** A **c** L **d** Q.

2 

The bag contains white (W), grey (G) and black (B) marbles.
A marble is selected at random from the bag.
Write down the probability that the marble is:

a white **b** grey **c** black **d** pink

e not white **f** not grey **g** not black **h** not pink.

3 12 13 14 15 16 17 18 19

A card is selected at random from this set of eight cards.
Write down the probability that the number on the card is:

a an odd number **b** a prime number **c** a multiple of 3

d less than 20 **e** greater than 14 **f** a factor of 100.

4 

A shape is selected at random from this set of seven shapes.
Write down the probability that the shape is:

a black **b** grey **c** a pentagon

d a hexagon **e** a black pentagon **f** a grey hexagon

g a black hexagon **h** a black octagon.

5 **a** Helen throws a biased four-sided dice 20 times.
The results are shown in the table.

Score	1	2	3	4
Frequency	5	4	5	6

Write down the experimental probability of throwing a 4 with this dice. Write your answer as a decimal.

b Richard throws the same four-sided dice 200 times.
The results are shown in the table.

Score	1	2	3	4
Frequency	48	21	61	70

Write down the new experimental probability of throwing a 4 with this dice. Write your answer as a decimal.

c Which of the two experimental probabilities in parts **a** and **b** do you think is closest to the theoretical probability? Explain your answer.

15D Combined events

Example

Robert picks a piece of fruit at random from a bag containing one apple (A), one banana (B) and one orange (O).

He also picks a sandwich at random from a bag containing one cheese sandwich (C), one salad sandwich (S) and one tuna sandwich (T).

a List all the possible outcomes.
b Write down the probability of picking an apple and a tuna sandwich.

---

a The possible outcomes are:

AC AS AT
BC BS BT
OC OS OT

b $P(AT) = \frac{1}{9}$

1 Anna has two bags.
Each bag contains one red (R), one blue (B) and one yellow (Y) marble.
She picks a marble at random from each bag.

a Copy and complete this two-way table to show all the possible outcomes.

		Bag 2		
		B	**R**	**Y**
Bag 1	**B**	B, B		
	R			R, Y
	Y			

b Write down the probability of picking:

i two blue marbles

ii two marbles of the same colour

iii two marbles of different colours

iv at least one red marble.

2 The Venn diagram shows information about the types of website visited by a group of students.

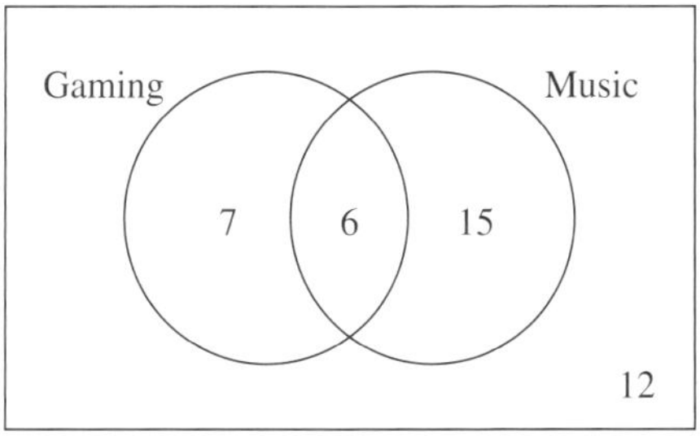

One of these students is selected at random.

Find the probability that this person:

a visits both gaming and music websites

b visits gaming but not music websites

c visits music websites

d visits neither gaming nor music websites.

3 The spinner can land on either black or white.

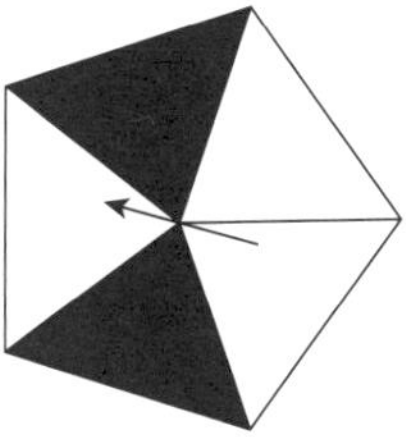

a Draw a tree diagram to represent the outcomes of spinning the spinner twice.

b Use your tree diagram to find the probability that the spinner lands on the same colour on both spins.

4 Three coins are thrown to see whether each coin lands heads up (H) or tails up (T).

a List all the possible outcomes.

b What is the probability of throwing

i three heads

ii at least two tails?

16A–16C Introduction to vectors

Example

Draw the vector $\begin{pmatrix} -6 \\ 2 \end{pmatrix}$

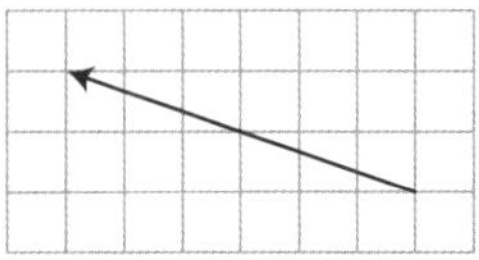

1 Write these vectors as column vectors.

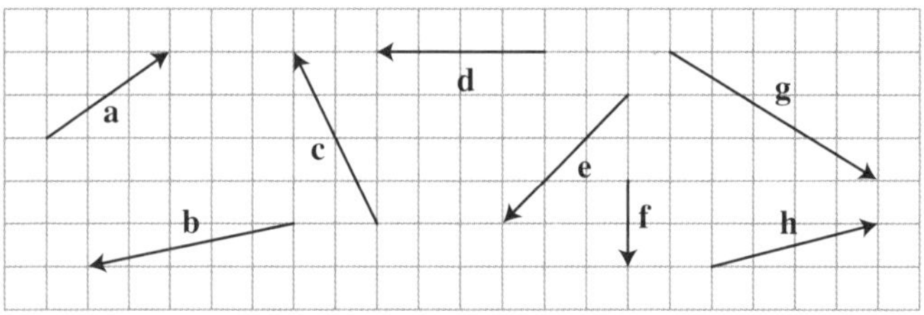

2 Draw these vectors on grid paper.

a $\begin{pmatrix} -2 \\ 1 \end{pmatrix}$ **b** $\begin{pmatrix} -4 \\ 2 \end{pmatrix}$ **c** $\begin{pmatrix} 5 \\ 2 \end{pmatrix}$ **d** $\begin{pmatrix} 2 \\ -5 \end{pmatrix}$

e What do you notice about the vectors in parts **a** and **b**?

f What do you notice about the vectors in parts **c** and **d**?

3 $\mathbf{p} = \begin{pmatrix} 4 \\ 1 \end{pmatrix}$ $\mathbf{q} = \begin{pmatrix} 2 \\ -3 \end{pmatrix}$

Draw a diagram to find $\mathbf{p} + \mathbf{q}$.

4 $\mathbf{p} = \begin{pmatrix} 3 \\ 2 \end{pmatrix}$ $\mathbf{q} = \begin{pmatrix} 1 \\ 5 \end{pmatrix}$ $\mathbf{r} = \begin{pmatrix} 4 \\ 0 \end{pmatrix}$

Write these as column vectors:

a $\mathbf{p} + \mathbf{q}$ **b** $\mathbf{q} + \mathbf{r}$ **c** $\mathbf{r} - \mathbf{p}$ **d** $\mathbf{p} + \mathbf{q} - \mathbf{r}$

e $2\mathbf{p} + 2\mathbf{q}$ **f** $7\mathbf{r} + \mathbf{p}$ **g** $\mathbf{q} - 3\mathbf{r}$ **h** $5\mathbf{p} + 4\mathbf{q} - 3\mathbf{r}$

i $2\mathbf{p} + 3\mathbf{q}$ **j** $5\mathbf{q} - 2\mathbf{r}$ **k** $\mathbf{r} - 2\mathbf{p}$ **l** $3\mathbf{r} - 5\mathbf{q}$

5 $\mathbf{p} = \begin{pmatrix} -4 \\ 1 \end{pmatrix}$ $\mathbf{q} = \begin{pmatrix} 0 \\ -3 \end{pmatrix}$ $\mathbf{r} = \begin{pmatrix} -7 \\ -3 \end{pmatrix}$

Write these as column vectors:

a $\mathbf{p} + \mathbf{q}$ **b** $\mathbf{q} + 2\mathbf{r}$ **c** $3\mathbf{r} - \mathbf{q}$ **d** $\mathbf{p} + \mathbf{q} + \mathbf{r}$

e $2\mathbf{p} + 2\mathbf{r}$ **f** $5\mathbf{r} + \mathbf{q}$ **g** $2\mathbf{q} - 3\mathbf{r}$ **h** $\mathbf{p} - 2\mathbf{q} + 3\mathbf{r}$

i $3\mathbf{p} + 2\mathbf{q}$ **j** $^{-}\mathbf{q} - 2\mathbf{r}$ **k** $^{-}2\mathbf{r} + 3\mathbf{p}$ **l** $^{-}\mathbf{r} + 2\mathbf{q}$

6 Find the values of x and y when:

a $\begin{pmatrix} x \\ y \end{pmatrix} + \begin{pmatrix} 4 \\ 1 \end{pmatrix} = \begin{pmatrix} 6 \\ 8 \end{pmatrix}$ **b** $\begin{pmatrix} 5 \\ y \end{pmatrix} + \begin{pmatrix} x \\ 2 \end{pmatrix} = \begin{pmatrix} 9 \\ 7 \end{pmatrix}$

c $\begin{pmatrix} x \\ 2 \end{pmatrix} + \begin{pmatrix} 9 \\ -3 \end{pmatrix} = \begin{pmatrix} 2 \\ y \end{pmatrix}$ **d** $4\begin{pmatrix} 3 \\ y \end{pmatrix} - 5\begin{pmatrix} x \\ 1 \end{pmatrix} = \begin{pmatrix} 2 \\ -17 \end{pmatrix}$

16D–16E Using vectors in geometry

Example

ABCD is a trapezium.

$\overrightarrow{AB} = 2\mathbf{p}$, $\overrightarrow{DC} = \mathbf{p}$ and $\overrightarrow{DA} = \mathbf{q}$

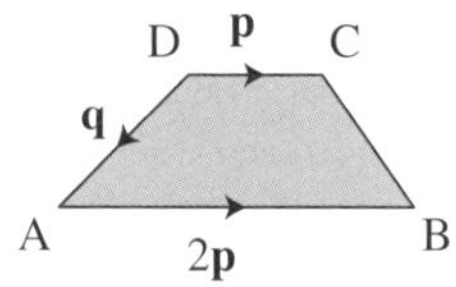

Find in terms of **p** and **q**:

a $\overrightarrow{BA}$ **b** $\overrightarrow{DB}$ **c** $\overrightarrow{CA}$ **d** $\overrightarrow{CB}$

---

a $\overrightarrow{BA} = {}^{-}2\mathbf{p}$ **b** $\overrightarrow{DB} = \overrightarrow{DA} + \overrightarrow{AB} = \mathbf{q} + 2\mathbf{p}$

c $\overrightarrow{CA} = \overrightarrow{CD} + \overrightarrow{DA} = {}^{-}\mathbf{p} + \mathbf{q} = \mathbf{q} - \mathbf{p}$

d $\overrightarrow{CB} = \overrightarrow{CD} + \overrightarrow{DA} + \overrightarrow{AB} = {}^{-}\mathbf{p} + \mathbf{q} + 2\mathbf{p} = \mathbf{p} + \mathbf{q}$

1

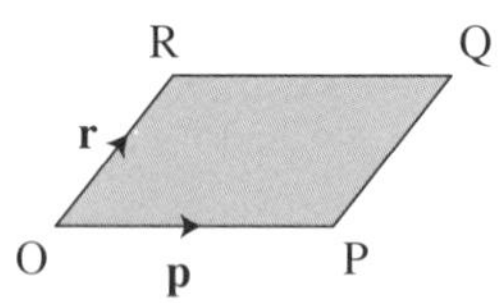

OPQR is a parallelogram. $\overrightarrow{OP} = \mathbf{p}$ and $\overrightarrow{OR} = \mathbf{r}$

Find in terms of **p** and **r**:

a $\overrightarrow{RQ}$ **b** $\overrightarrow{QP}$ **c** $\overrightarrow{OQ}$ **d** $\overrightarrow{PR}$

2

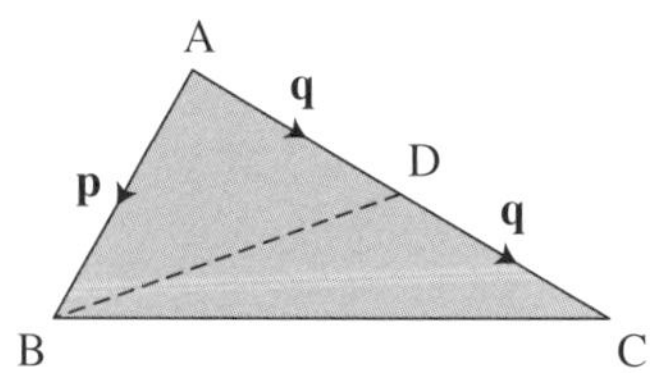

ABC is a triangle. D is the midpoint of AC. $\overrightarrow{AB} = \mathbf{p}$ and $\overrightarrow{AD} = \overrightarrow{DC} = \mathbf{q}$

Find in terms of **p** and **q**:

a $\overrightarrow{DA}$ **b** $\overrightarrow{AC}$ **c** $\overrightarrow{BD}$ **d** $\overrightarrow{CB}$

3 OPQR is a square. M is the midpoint of PQ.

$\overrightarrow{OP} = \mathbf{p}$ and $\overrightarrow{OR} = \mathbf{r}$

Find in terms of **p** and **r**:

a $\overrightarrow{OQ}$ **b** $\overrightarrow{PM}$ **c** $\overrightarrow{OM}$ **d** $\overrightarrow{MR}$

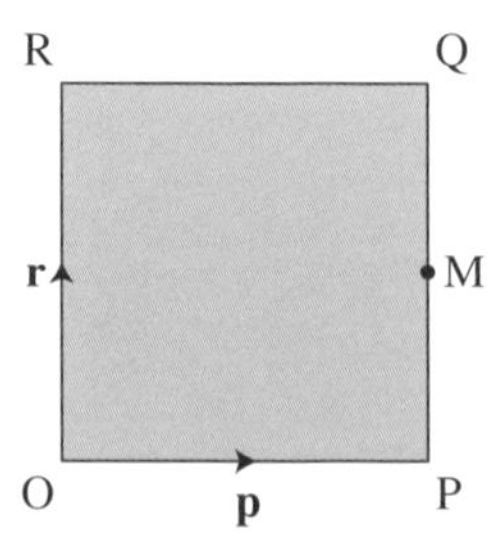

4 Write down the position vectors of the points A, B, C, D, E, F and G.

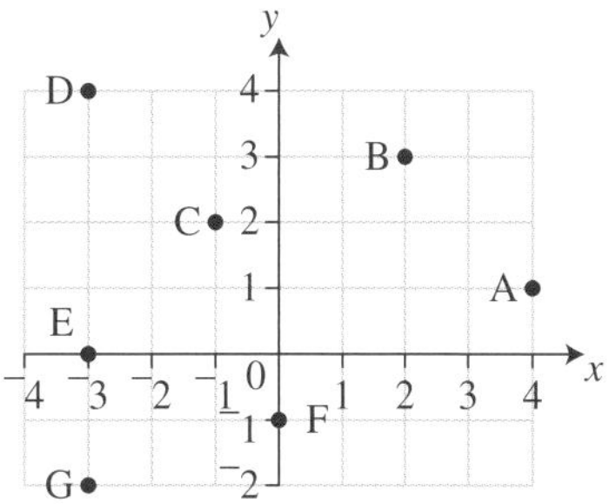

5 ABCD is a parallelogram. Three of the four vertices of ABCD are:
A = (1, 3), B = (9, 4) and C = (10, 7).

a Write $\overrightarrow{AB}$ as a column vector.

b Write $\overrightarrow{BC}$ as a column vector.

c Write $\overrightarrow{AD}$ as a column vector.

d Write down the position vector of the point D.

6 A = (5, 3), $\overrightarrow{AB} = \begin{pmatrix} 5 \\ ^{-}2 \end{pmatrix}$ and $\overrightarrow{BC} = \begin{pmatrix} 2 \\ 3 \end{pmatrix}$

a Write down the position vector of point A.

b Find the position vectors of points B and C.

7 A = (2, 1) and B = (8, 4)
Find the coordinates of the point P which divides the line segment AB in the ratio 2 : 1.